Volume One

PAGE ONE

AN

ANTHOLOGY

By *Newfoundland West Coast Writers*

175

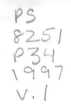

PAGE ONE DIGEST
Volume I

An Anthology of Creative Writing

from Newfoundland's West Coast

**Published by
Cabbltt Productions**

**Printed by
Dicks and Company Limited**

CABBITT PRODUCTIONS
P.O. Box 3036
Deer Lake, NF   Canada A0K 2E0

Cover and Book Design: Janalee Amelia Strowbridge
Printing and Binding: Dicks and Company Limited

The opinions of any individual author are not necessarily those of the Page One group or the publisher.

Canadian Cataloguing in Publication Data
Main entry under title: Page One Digest

ISBN 0-9682182-0-2

1. Canadian literature (English) —20th Century
PS8251.P34 1997   C810.8'0054   C97-900515-9
PR9194.9.P34 1997

ACKNOWLEDGEMENTS

Cabbitt Productions acknowledges the financial support of the Newfoundland and Labrador Arts Council and the Cabot 500 Corporation for A Year of the Arts 1997 Project. We also acknowledge contributions by the Governments of Canada and Newfoundland and Labrador, NewTel and Human Resources Development Canada. These have all helped make this publication possible.

We gratefully acknowledge the following for varied support:

- Twyla Loder, Student Worker
- Several contributing writers for compiling and pre-editing
- Sheila Robinson for editing, formatting and preparing the document for publishing
- Gary King for editing
- Deer Lake Public Library and Ralph Purcell for library facilities
- Driftwood Inn, Pizza Delight, Deer Lake Motel
- Arts & Culture Centre
- Grand Lake Centre of Economic Development
- CBC, CFCB, and KIXX
- Deborah Lynn Thomas for publicity and support
- Carolyn Shoemaker for graphics design
- Victoria Young for the Cabbitt design
- *The Compass* (March 25, 1987 and April 1, 1987 editions), *The St. John's Metro* (July 3, 1983 edition) and *The Lakeside Press* (October 7, 1988 edition) for use of previously published material

INTRODUCTION

Welcome to the pages of the first Page One Digest! Page One is a writers' group formed in 1987. This group exists to encourage writing, to offer constructive criticism, to listen to each other, to read our work, to stimulate ideas, and to accept each other.

Page One Digest is a collection of works from writers who live or have lived in the area of Newfoundland between Corner Brook and Woody Point. There are works from junior high students, from seniors and from people of all ages in between.

This digest represents life from numerous viewpoints and life styles. Inside these pages, you will read work from beginning writers and from writers who have made writing a part of daily life for many years. All enjoy putting words on paper and sharing ideas with each other and with you, the readers of our first published collection.

This anthology celebrates the continued existence of this group and the perseverance of writers who write, not to get rich or famous (although that would be nice), but because they must.

DEDICATION

To Our Readers

Contents

From Whence We Came:

Family Sagas:

Loving, Losing and Learning

Ben's Story
Nellie P. Strowbridge

Young Ben was left motherless when he was a baby. His young mother had given birth to him in her sister's house. Her one relief was that she no longer had to wear gunshot in her shoes, a penalty imposed by an elderly priest for her act of fornication. Still, there was the constant pain of feeling less of a human being for having been caught out of wedlock. Finally, when her son was six months old, she laid him in a wooden box used as his cradle, and left him. She walked out into the night. Then she started to run, making long strides as she ran across a partially frozen pond, leaving black footprints in the melting snow before she disappeared. She may not have realized that her son would suffer more, and that his life would have less value without her in it.

Young Ben never knew that his mother had 'destroyed' herself. A bastard he was and bastard he was called more than once by people in the community where he grew up. In return for his keep at the house of one relative and then another, Ben brought water, cleaved wood, and kept the wood box filled. During the winter months he shivered in his flour bag underwear as he lit the fire in the kitchen stove so that the rest of the family could get up to a warm house. No one knew if Ben had ever been beaten or tongue-lashed. He was largely ignored as he grew up among relatives. The "stranger" element in his flesh and blood, of the father no one seemed to know, set him apart.

Aunt Clotilda finally took Ben in. She must have thought that someone like him would have the strain of tuberculosis, or of some other disease that was on the go at the time. Whatever her reasons, whenever he sat for his meals, Ben was given a spot at one corner of the table, along with his own dish and cutlery. When he got up from the table, his aunt would wipe his seat—behind his back at first, then in front of his face. Ben never seemed to notice. It was as if he had come to accept himself as less than other people.

Ben watched his peers grow up and fall in love, yet he showed no interest in the opposite sex. Perhaps he had no love to give. It would seem that way by the empty look in his eyes. You would think that someone would have shown him a little love. He went to church all his life. There, he might have felt God's love if he had not been constantly reminded that people who do not behave are going to Hell. He may have thought that he wasn't behaving just by the looks his relatives gave him.

Ben did not go to work when he grew up. He continued to take care of his aunt and uncle's house, while his Uncle Max, who suffered from back trouble, sat around the house passing the time of day with other unemployed men.

No one seemed to wonder what Ben was thinking. People treated him as if his mind were a blank sheet of paper that didn't need anything written on it. He was used to people not talking to him, which may have been why he didn't talk to them. Now and then when a stranger passed through the community and spoke to Ben, he would start talking and keep on as long as he had an ear. Perhaps he hoped that someone would turn up as his father. After many years someone did, but the elder Ben never bothered with his son. He died and left a lot of money for relatives to fight over—relatives who didn't care that Ben went empty-handed.

Sometimes, even when he was grown, you could see Ben sitting with his small, thin knees tight together, hugging himself as if he were the only comfort he had. He died when he was fifty—to the surprise of his aunt and uncle, who did not know that he was sick. They had long concluded, though, that he did not have much life. They put him in a coffin, and a hole was dug for him in the corner of the church graveyard. He got the same six feet as everyone else, and when he was buried, no one could tell that he was not equal to everyone else. Not until they put his marker down. It bore only his name, as if he belonged to no one.

"You done yer best fer him, maid," a neighbour said to Clotilda after the funeral, and Clotilda held her head high, as if she had just been crowned. Yes, she had done her duty in rearing her sister's son. She sniffled a little as she went home. After all, even someone who is "just there" for such a long time leaves an emptiness. She looked at Ben's dishes and seat that she had washed for the last time.

Love must have touched Ben in some form, perhaps in the smell of a flower, fresh air and in the songs of birds. Maybe his memory had carried shadows of his mother's love. It would seem that way, because when Clotilda cleaned his room, she found a wooden box under his bed. It held a scribbler full of poems he had written. She looked through the poems, and for the first time, Ben came alive to her, as someone with a heart and mind and not just as a soul to be redeemed or lost.

She could have wondered if Ben had almost become a "deaf and dumb mute" by being ignored—but it seems she didn't. After scanning some of his poems, she threw them under the damper of her kitchen stove. After all, Ben would not be needing them anymore.

Visitors noticed the box that held Ben's poems just as Max was going to cut it up for firewood. They were awed by the beautiful carvings of flowers, birds and angels on its sides. When they asked if they could have it, Clotilda grabbed it from under Max's raised axe. She took it, scoured it and put it back under the bed.

For the first time she had found a part of Ben that she seemed to think had value.

Me Hog, Me Wife, A Wolf and Me
Jean Legge Hiscock

At four o'clock this morning,
I'm walking across the bog;
Me wife is tending the children,
While I attend the hog.

I'm thinking of the howling wolf
I heard outside last night,
And praying to the Lord above,
Me pig will be all right.

He'll give us winter bacon,
Ham and salt pork, too;
And when nothing else is left of him
His bones will make the stew.

The sun's asleep this morning,
And the wind is mighty cold;
Ah, there's me pig inside his pen
With no sign of a hole.

He's slipping and he's sliding,
Knee-deep in black turf bog;
I wish I had no more worries
Than me careless, dirty hog.

I'd best get home to me cabin
Soon as this piggy's fed;
Me wife will be washing the babes
And making up our bed.

16

"A man's house is his castle"
Is what they always say;
My castle's roof got a hole in it—
'Twas rotten anyway.

Funny I didn't see the hole
When I set out this morn;
I was thinking of me old fat hog
And scared his pen was torn.

I walk up to the wretched door
And soon I am inside;
"Woman o' mine, you're awful quiet—
Where on earth you bide?"

"Now what's the meaning of this blood
Trailing across the floor?
And this wet and bloody bedclothes
Scattered 'round and tore?"

I left me wife and children
And walked across the bog;
And now a wolf has eat them,
And I just got me hog.

Making it Right
W. Rex Stirling

Carl checked the shelf above his bunk for the final time. "Yeah, I got everything," he muttered to himself. Sitting down, he took a cigarette from his shirt pocket, lit it, and leaned back against the cell wall and peered pensively at the barred window. In an hour or so, he thought, some other poor slob will be a guest in the big house. He remembered all the times he had lain on the thin, lumpy mattress, his eyes closed, mentally escaping the prison which had held him captive for fifteen years.

Throwing the half-smoked cigarette to the concrete floor, Carl crushed it out with his foot. Memories became images of other times and places. Paula would be twenty now. How often he had tried to form a picture of her in his mind as a young woman. When he'd last seen her she was a happy five year old with bouncing blond pigtails and sparkling blue eyes, trying her best to be all grown up and not cry.

Her daddy was going away; she knew that, but she didn't understand why. How do you tell a trusting five year old that you are responsible for her mother's death? That guilt eats away at you. What do you say?

"Well, you see, honey, your mommy and daddy were driving home from Corner Brook. It was snowing heavily and the highway was slippery. Both of us were very tired. We should have stopped to rest, but we didn't; your daddy lost control of the car, and, well . . . ."

His wife's screams as the car spiralled over the guardrail still echoed in Carl's ears. Yeah, how do you explain that to a five-year-old kid? Do you say: "That's what happened, and I got to leave you here with your Aunt Josie and Uncle Ed because I can't look after you"?

Carl stood up, walked slowly to the cell window and looked intently through the bars. It didn't work, he thought to himself; it didn't work at all. After the accident, he had spent the next three years wandering around various parts of the mainland and the U.S.

One day, thirsty and road-weary, he went into a tavern for a beer. At the far end of the bar was a big, loud-mouthed man, the kind who enjoys intimidating everyone with his size. As Carl approached the man on his way to the rest room, he tripped over a foot which had been stuck out, intentionally, he was sure. Only fast thinking in grabbing a nearby table prevented him from falling.

"Why don't you watch where you're going you stupid jerk?" the big man bellowed. Carl stared at his tormentor for a few seconds. His first instinct was to ignore the troublemaker, so he turned toward the rest rooms again.

The big man persisted. "All you dumb hicks are as clumsy as you are ugly," he roared.

Carl's shoulders sagged, not out of fear, but rather from the feeling of being forced into doing something he'd rather not do. Suddenly the bar became very quiet, as everyone braced themselves for the trouble they knew was soon to erupt. Carl had a simple philosophy in situations like this: if you can't avoid a fight, give it all you've got.

The next morning he woke up in a jail cell. Pain raced through his head. He was pressing his fingers to his temples in an effort to ease the agony when an RCMP constable walked into his cell.

"What happened, Constable?"

"You don't remember?"

"Nah, not really. Just some big loudmouth looking for trouble."

"That's too bad, because you killed the loudmouth."

Carl sat in shocked silence for several minutes. Finally he spoke.

"Geez, Constable, that can't be right, it can't."

"I'm afraid so. He's dead all right."

"How did it happen?"

"Stabbed in the neck with a broken beer bottle. He bled to death on the way to the hospital."

"That's crazy! I was drinkin' beer out of a can."

"So you say. Witnesses claim otherwise."

Carl rubbed his forehead and looked at the Mountie in disbelief. "Tell me you're putting me on, Constable?"

"I wish I could."

"But I've never killed anyone—never!"

"Doesn't matter if I believe you or not. That's up to a judge and jury, if you elect to have one. I hope you can afford a good lawyer. If not, one will be appointed for you."

"They'll believe me because it's the truth," Carl declared.

"Let's hope for your sake that they do," replied the Mountie.

Carl sat in his cell muttering to himself. "They'll believe me; I just know they will."

But the jury didn't. The verdict was involuntary manslaughter; the sentence: fifteen to twenty years in Dorchester Penitentiary.

The anger inside Carl raged for five long years before he was forced to accept the fact that the only way to get out, without serving his full term, was to conform to prison rules and regulations. He spent the next three years getting a high school diploma, learning a trade, and staying out of trouble. The warden was so impressed with the paintings Carl had produced in art class that he put several on display in the visitors' lounge. All had sold, and soon Carl had three thousand dollars credited to him in the prison accounts department.

Six months before the fifteenth anniversary of his sentence, Carl was granted an unconditional parole. He was a free man once more. With his release he carried a dream of being reunited with Paula.

One of the first stops Carl made was to a used car lot where he found the car he wanted. The used car salesman looked at Carl warily. "Well, I don't know," he said. "The boss told me not to let her go for less than three thousand; he's not in today, so I can't check out your offer."

"Look man," Carl said desperately, "I gotta' have a car, and twenty-five hundred is my limit. Geez, that's all it's worth."

The salesman stood there stroking his chin, wondering if his boss would give him hell for selling the old Chevy at barely over cost. But it had been sitting on the lot for a long time, and a sale was a sale. He might even be able to squeeze a small commission out of the deal.

"You've bought yourself a car," he told Carl.

The 1957 Chevy reminded Carl of one that he owned years ago. Sure, there was some rust around the rocker panels and fender wells, but it ran fine, and he didn't doubt for a moment that it would get him home to Newfoundland. The bright lights of the Irving service station reminded him that he needed gas. His stomach reminded him that he hadn't eaten since leaving prison. While he ate his burger and fries, he began to formulate a plan. He'd get a job, clean up his act, find his daughter and be the sort of father he should have been. If I don't settle down, he thought, I'll be back on the road again. That thought filled him with sadness. Fifteen years wasted, just like that—time he could never get back. He felt guilty for deserting his only child. He had left her with an elderly aunt and uncle. He had to make it up to her.

The small western Newfoundland community of Howley was very much like others of its size in the province. Fifteen years had made only a slight difference. The roads were paved now, and there was a mini shopping mall. Carl stopped the car a few hundred feet from the house. The vinyl siding was new, as was the chain link fence. Everything else was as he remembered it. He sat in the car, wondering what to do. Josie and Ed had never liked him very much. They had blamed him for the accident, and ending up in prison on a murder rap had been the last straw. They told him as much in the only letter they had sent. There was no point in stirring up old hatreds, and he wasn't in the mood for a lecture. He'd have to figure out another way to see his daughter.

Turning the ignition key, Carl backed up the old Chevy and drove to the local lunch counter for a coffee; there he bought a copy of *The Humber Log*. Suddenly, his eyes caught a picture with a brief article underneath. He read it over and over. There was no mistaking it—there she was. Carl stared at the picture and began to read: "Mr. and Mrs. Edward Blanford of Howley, are pleased to announce the forthcoming marriage of their niece Paula Denise Comerford to Weston Derrick Hounsell of St. John's, on the tenth of April in the Pentecostal Church,

Howley at three o'clock p.m."

The rest of the article became blurred and unimportant to Carl. Today was the tenth! He glanced at the clock above the counter: 2:30. He paid for his coffee and went outside.

Ten minutes later he was parked outside the Pentecostal church, trying to decide his next move. People entering the church gave him a curious look as they passed by.

There she was! There was absolutely no doubt in Carl's mind; it was Paula. She was a dead ringer for her mother. To his utter amazement, she turned from her bridesmaids when she saw him and walked over to where he sat in the car.

"That's a '57 Chevy Bel-Aire, isn't it?" she asked.

Carl looked into her deep blue eyes. They seemed to stare right through him. He was glad he was wearing sunglasses. He realized that he hadn't answered her question.

"It is a '57 Chevy Bel-Aire, isn't it?" she repeated.

"Oh, yes; yes, it is."

"My dad had a car just like this one. He used to take me for rides in it when I was a little girl."

"Where's your dad now?"

"I don't know—maybe on the mainland or in the States. He left home when I was five."

"You're getting married today? You look very beautiful."

Carl tried desperately to collect his wits. "Who am I kidding?" he thought. "I can't settle down, not anymore. Go to work? Keep regular hours? That's not for me, not after fifteen years in stir. I'd go nuts!" But he couldn't leave, not just yet; he owed it to her. She was, after all, his daughter, and his responsibility—even if she was about to be married. He had to tell her the truth, and it had to be now.

"Do you ever think about your dad coming back someday, getting a job here, being a father to you like a man should?" he asked.

"Yes, sometimes," she answered, her face pensive. "But I know why he left. He and mom had an accident; she was killed, and he never forgave himself. He knew he couldn't take care of me, so he left me in the care of my Uncle and Aunt Blanford. I have my own life now, and in a little while I'll be Mrs. Hounsell. Dad has his own life, too, and, wherever he is, I hope he's happy and doing what he wants to be doing."

Carl felt pride swell up inside him. She was exactly like her mother, and she was getting married at the same age. He had been wrong, so very wrong. He now knew there was no need to tell her who he was.

"Paula, it's time to go in now."

She glanced in the direction of the voice, then back at Carl. "I've got to go. Stay safe."

With a wave of her hand, she ran toward the church. Carl smiled with satisfaction, then he started the engine. He put the car in gear and drove off, heading west.

Paula stood for a brief moment in the doorway of the church and watched as the old Chevy and its driver disappeared from view. She spoke aloud in a hushed whisper, "Take good care of him, God, wherever he goes." Fighting back a tear she added, "I love you, Daddy, and I always have."

Prisoner of Love
(for Julian)
Terry G. Manuel

Prisoner of love behind the walls of Her Majesty's
Penitentiary.
I was loving you and
I bet you never knew about me loving you like I do, like I
do.
It came about ten months before I got out.
I was loving you and I bet you never knew.

What can be done about a Dad loving his son?
Like I do, like I do?

Julian, in my arms I can't hold you right now
and tell you that I love you.
If it could be done,
I would truly tell you that I love you, my son.

But it can't, it can't be done, my darling son.

Julian, I love you.

Raising Kids and Goldfish
Nellie P. Strowbridge

I once heard someone say that people who don't like animals are cold fish. I don't know what he'd say about someone who doesn't like goldfish. W-e-l-l, it's not that I don't like the tiny creatures. I like them when they are living at some place other than my house.

Goldfish are not that friendly. They never try to get to know you. They don't talk, bark or beg for food. They wiggle around a bit, but it's hard to understand their body language.

Birds, at least, provide another use for paper such as this, and dogs and cats communicate even if it is with growls and hisses. When my children, Michael and Janalee, were small, they had their cat standing on two legs hoping it would do at three years what they had managed to do at one year—walk on two legs.

It was a cornflakes box that got the kids interested in goldfish. They could cut out three fish tags, take them to a patron pet shop and—presto!—be the owners of one free goldfish. What could be cheaper than a goldfish? Certainly not the container of pepper-like food, nor an aquarium, which I put off buying until I was satisfied that if it didn't have nine lives, it, at least, had one long one.

The kids worried that their goldfish would get car-sick on the way home, then I worried about the mess the kids were making trying to acclimatize the fish. First one bowl for the fish and its original water, then another bowl filled with new water, and a soup ladle to dip from one bowl into the other.

Once we got the goldfish settled in its new home—an

amber brandy snifter—it started sniffing around, perhaps looking for something fishless to eat. The brandy snifter made the fish look big in the sides from the outside, and soon the kids predicted that the goldfish was going to have babies.

"Babies," I sighed. "More mouths to feed."

"No, Mom. The fish can share," Michael decided.

He had swallowed the line: "Two or more can live as cheaply as one."

I never thought that a goldfish would bring the heads of two siblings together in provocative interaction, but there they were, one asking the other, "Would you have liked to have been born a goldfish?", and the other spitting one word: "Ugh!"

"So you think you're better than a goldfish," the first accused.

"Well, I don't have eyes on the side of my head, a pointed face, and kidneys that show through the skin. Two legs are better than a tail, and I'm not wet all the time. That fish must feel like a prune."

"At least the fish is always clean. It doesn't have to take baths or brush its teeth. That saves time."

"Yeah, time for what? Fish can't even tell time. And they are poor."

"Poor!"

"Yeah, they don't own anything, not even clothes."

Once the two kids got over their discussion, they started observing the fish. The fish swallowed and Janalee thought it was trying to tell her something; it moved its tail and Michael thought it was waving—or getting hyper. They argued about whether it was a boy or girl—a crucial point for kids trying to decide on a name.

They finally decided to call it by its proper name: Goldfish.

Janalee admonished Michael not to play with Goldfish, or take it out and dry it off. Because fish like to be wet. Then she brought the cat to view its rival and to warn it that Goldfish was not to be had for lunch. The cat didn't seem to be listening. It was too busy sniffing the air.

Twenty-four hours passed. The next thing I knew Janalee was running toward me with the brandy snifter— the water and the fish inside flopping dangerously close to the edge. "The fish is dead!" she sobbed.

I looked at it. "It's not belly-up, so it can't be dead. It must be sleeping."

"Sleeping!" she said suspiciously. "Its eyes aren't closed."

"That's because it has no eyelids to speak of."

"It's not breathing," she insisted.

"How can you tell?" I asked. "Have you felt its pulse?"

"Never mind, I know it's dead, and you killed it by ignoring it and making it feel unwelcomed."

"So it up-and-died to get attention." I sounded too sarcastic for my own liking.

Michael tried to come to my rescue by suggesting that perhaps it was old—even if it wasn't gray.

I felt kind of sad when I pronounced Goldfish dead, but I promised an inquiry into its death.

It was the least I could do.

A Mother's Cry
Florence Antle

Does anyone understand a mother's lament
When she believes her children are heaven sent,
And the wrong things they do aren't really meant?
It's so easy to smile and then relent.

Does anyone understand a mother's woes?
Are her children her enemies or her foes?
The Lord above is the only one who knows,
For what one reaps he also sows.

Does anyone understand a mother's cries
When children do wrong and then tell lies?
At times she just can't believe her eyes.
She just shakes her head and looks to the skies.

Daddy's Girl
Amanda Caravan

I gave her a hug
and told that her she's my friend;
no matter what she decided to do,
we would be friends 'til the end.

I told her she should tell someone
what her daddy does
when he's had too much to drink
or when he has a buzz.

She said she's Daddy's Girl—
she can't do that to him;
I told her to think about what he does to her
when he hits her with his fist.

She came to my house full of bruises,
scratches and little cuts;
her arms were full of cigarette burns
from when he would dout his butts.

She had to do something,
but how could I get her to tell?
I thought about telling someone myself,
to get her out of this hell.

Her father used to be so nice,
a perfect husband and dad;
but then he turned to the bottle
and became someone so bad.

I want her out of such a life;
I don't want her black and blue;
I wonder if she will tell someone;
I wonder what she will do.

Learning the Wind:

Knowing our Island

The Humber
Vaughn Harbin

The Humber winds its way along
Through stony hills and lush green vales,
Past fertile farmlands tilled and kept,
Beside tall stands of silver birch,
Midst maple groves and alder guards—
Beneath whose branches mayflowers bloom;
And ever as it wends its way,
The logs drift on and children play.

The river follows its chosen course,
while man-made highways rise nearby,
And overhead strong eagles watch
The field mice dart from rock to rock;
The Humber's banks now soft, now sharp,
Now deepening cleft, now gentle beach;
And ever as it wends its way,
The logs drift on and children play.

It whirls a devilish dancing pool
And tumbles past small Shellbird Isle;
Beneath the mountain's weathered face
It hurries to its destined place,
Under stout bridges on pillars strong,
Surging forward, moving on;
And ever as it wends its way
The logs drift on and children play.

The river slows its pace at times,
As if it, too, has need of rest,

Yet never fully stops its flow—
It has to move, it seems to know
That even it has rules to keep.
Through circling seasons life goes on;
And ever as it wends its way,
The logs drift on and children play.

Man in the Mountain
Vaughn Harbin

The mountain's face looks down today,
As it has for ages now.
Each passing car that winds its way
Beneath its shadowed brow
Receives in turn the stoic stare
Of that form worn bleak and bare.
A joke of nature played by chance
This face above the Devil's Dance?
Or another reminder from above
That God yet looks on man with love?
Methinks the former well could be,
And yet, the thought of Deity
Enthroned above such devilry
Brings the truth home clearly, joke or no:
Where God is not, men cannot go!

Hook and Release
Stacey M. Hiscock

I am a fish,
Caught today for the sixth time.
Such a clever fish
I was,
Fighting and struggling,
Each time managing
To get away.

But I'm old and tired
Now.
I feel no need to go on
Living like this,
My skin hanging in strips,
Infested with sea-lice,
My gills breathing in
All this horrible oxygen.

So, this time
Fight, I do not;
Struggle, I need not.
'Tis better to go now
Than to suffer, only to get caught
Again.

My body is deteriorated
To almost nothing.
I just stay at ease,
Without moving,
And be.

Be caught;
Be supper for some fisherman.

So, ready to give up
As you can imagine,
It took me by surprise
When, instead of keeping me with pride—
As a trophy—
The fisherman
Set me free.

Journey of the North
Edith C. Johnson

It was as if there could be no end to the panoramic sight of the beautiful Long Range Mountains seeming to touch the sky. The Peninsula is seven thousand square miles of mountain slopes falling toward the Gulf of St. Lawrence and down to White Bay.

I am remembering a trip my husband, Roy, and I made by car: three hundred miles along the Great Northern Peninsula Highway, then still a secondary road, and then twenty miles by canoe via a river flowing into the sea at Main Brook, Hare Bay. We left Deer Lake at early morning, on the 10th of September.

In Autumn, when the days are getting shorter, the weather is usually fine and cool. It is the loveliest of the four seasons. Colours splash along the highways, in the valleys, and over the mountainside like a bright carpet. The scent of trees drifts on the quiet air.

The long drive down the peninsula was a fantastic

experience of high tablelands and peaks; it was not more than a score of miles from the sea, where most of the coastline is steep.

As we drove along the highway, villages and scenic vistas tempted us to stop and explore. One curve of the road brought to our view the beautiful East Arm of Bonne Bay and the steeply rising Kildevil Mountain. We came to a small roadside restaurant set in the midst of magnificent scenery. The dining room was nearly empty. We chose a table near the window. Through the window, we saw men fishing from small boats in the bay.

Restaurant walls and glass cases held many artifacts. I pointed to a birch bark canoe on a rack. We walked across the room to examine it and were told that it had been owned by the last Indian guide on the Northern Peninsula—and that it was the last canoe of its kind! The canoe almost looked as if it were a very old Indian, who was waiting to go to his happy hunting ground—its ribs stood out, and the birch bark was faded and old.

Once we were back on the highway, we saw ripples of water washing over a rugged rock in the inlet. One lone, graceful seagull posed atop the rock, as if waiting for a perceptive photographer.

We swung around a bend. We saw, a few miles away from us, an attractive white lighthouse, which had been trimmed a tidy red. We were driving along by the Gulf of St. Lawrence. Sea ducks, sitting on the water, bobbing up and down with the waves, ignored the hovering gulls, even when one would swoop down to snatch a fish from the sea.

After passing through several villages, we approached Western Brook, where, on windy days, mounds of white sand form snow-like drifts across the road and over the bog.

As we drove along, we crossed licensed rivers: River of Ponds, Torrent River, East River, and Castors River. On these rivers, during salmon season, anglers' leaders flicker their silver threads through bright sunlight.

It was exciting as we drew near Flowers Cove and looked across the Strait of Belle Isle to see the Quebec shore of Blanc Sablon.

About one mile from Castors Harbour, we came to the turn-off where the road went eastward. Hare Bay was 50 miles away. The crunch of gravel whirled and sprayed around the car wheels and struck the underside of the fenders.

We topped a hill. There before us spread Hare Bay. Far-off we saw speed boats swiftly moving about. We were nearing the end of our journey by car.

As we slowly drove down the hill, we soon reached the Bowater depot where we were to pick up a stove for our tent. It was supper time, always a good time to visit the cookhouse, with its rows of long tables set for a meal prepared by the camp cook and his staff. There was a choice of roast meat, pork or chicken, with delicious pastry pies and an attractive assortment of cookies and cakes.

After supper, we left for the river, over an old, abandoned, bumpy, twisted road.

A flight over the Great Northern Peninsula and its rivers in early autumn is a magnificent sight, but to outdoors people, travelling by canoe on a beautiful river gives even more pleasure. And canoe is the way we travelled up part of the Salmon River.

We put the canoe into the river at its widest part, prepared to paddle the long miles upstream. We were going to spend ten days alone, away from people and man-made noises. I smiled at the thought.

Roy sat in the stern of the canoe; I sat in the bow. We fell into a comfortable rhythm. Small puffs of clouds crowded across the sky. We had about two hours of paddling ahead.

The river is one quarter-mile wide in some places, its banks high and wooded. A moose gallantly stood on the shoreline. He watched our moving canoe for a moment, turned and at a slow pace, ran along the river bank for almost a mile, stopping often to look at us. Satisfied, he lifted his head high, then disappeared into the trees. We crept along, close to the river bank. Swirls of grass on top of the water floated like maidens' hair, coloured red, pink, yellow, orange, light green and dark green, streaming out with the tide as if a mermaid swam below.

A few yards away, a black duck quacked and flew up from the water, while a mother duck swam along with her brood to find cover in the brushwood.

Each new angle of the river brought us new visual delights. Where the bank sloped down to the river, beavers had built their lodge. A beaver swam along, slapped its tail loudly on the water, and vanished.

The sun was beginning to sink low in the sky when we arrived at a favourable clearing to pitch our tent. The shores of the river were unpopulated. The silence—and, even more, the solitude—was complete. The mountain pressed against the sky, with the river running along its base, looked proud, complete.

We set up the tent facing the river, sheltered among spruce and fir trees. We unloaded the canoe. Where was the stove?! Back at the depot in Hare Bay!

We took our places in the canoe and headed back. We arrived back at the depot and, with the stove secure, made our way back to the river again.

The navy blue sky above us was thick with brilliant starry gems. As we glided smoothly and swiftly along, the moon rose like a colourless sun behind the trees. Moonlit silver radiance poured over the river. We paddled all the way through moonbeams.

The air was still, as if it listened in its silent beauty. Neither Roy nor I spoke, fearful of breaking the night's tranquillity. Suddenly, a beaver flapped its tail on the water; another dived underneath the canoe and disappeared without a trace.

By the time we got back to the camp site, pulled the canoe up onto the shore and assembled our stove and tent, we were ready to crawl into our sleeping bags. What a sleepy, peaceful night it was! No din of traffic, just the sound of silence. A place to make a person feel glad to be alive.

Our day began when dawn filtered through the trees. Huddled in my warm sleeping bag, I indulged in one of my favourite pastimes: listening to the sound of outdoors. The twitter of birds, the ripple of the water and the whispering wind in the trees played for me an endless melody. I slipped out of my sleeping bag, hurriedly got dressed, went outside and thanked God for another day. And then I said, "Good morning, world!"

The pink glow of morning lit the sky. The sharp fragrance of evergreen trees blended with the drifting smoke from the camp stove. It was the beginning of more wonderful days to come.

The sun rose in the sky, and the mountain stood out

sharply as we paddled around the river, looking for the feeding place of geese and a place to make a gazer. Satisfied with our find, we went back to the tent for lunch.

The sun climbed higher and glowed in the burnished sky. We went down to the river and stood for a while by the canoe. The river moved clearly and swiftly along. We looked at the rising sun, slid the canoe into the water and moved out from the shore. The mountain bordering the far side of the river shone with the gold of the autumn's aspen leaves. The water's reflection was perfect; a photograph would fail to tell where mountain ended and mirror image began.

We glided past a beaver repairing his house. He scurried at the sound of our paddles. At the widest part of the river we went around little islands covered with shrubs.

Further along, we moved through large and small rock reefs where the water either flowed over the reef or around it with a dramatic grandeur. Large salmon swam through the shallow water or lay on the bottom. As the river narrowed, birds of different species perched quietly or swam along the gently flowing stream.

After supper, I sat by the river on a boulder. The sky glowed with the sun-filled clouds of evening. The air moved gently, caressingly. A flock of geese flew over the mountain.

Promptly before dawn next morning we stole across the river, pulled the canoe up onto the little island, got settled in our gazer, and waited for the birds to come. We couldn't make a slight sound or movement, fearful that the birds would turn away. Two or three hours is a long time for me to keep still. I felt myself sway, and, glory be, I was asleep on my feet!

Then the days flew by, as they always do when a holiday nears its end.

Some sunny afternoon or evening, I will once again sit by a river and watch it glide by at the foot of a mountain.

Ecstasy of Flight
Pamela Chynn

Seagull gliding in the sky,
spreading your wings,
travelling to lands foreign
to my dreams.
I am a scavenger
beneath
your sapphire waves
while you take
the heavens ransom
with your beauty;
although I am enlightened by you,
I am often over-shadowed by you
and in so much awe of you
that it turns to resentment,
as I feel your gracefulness mock
my clumsy heart
and taunt me with the truth
of how
freedom can sing a no more
beautiful song
than the ecstasy of flight.

Learning the Wind
Vaughn Harbin

Strong northern gales
From old pirate tales
To make your skin
Crawl at night;
Overcast skies
And breakers that rise
To dash great grey rocks
In sorrowful might;
Lonely seagulls
In motionless flight,
O'er an ocean
Emerald bright,
Sporting the flash
Of many a wave
And crested with
A cap of white;
These are images
I have retained
From my boyhood days—
Days freely spent
Following the wind,
Learning his migrant ways.

Nature
Terri Moores

As the wind whispers
A sweet, soft song,
My heart grieves
For a better tomorrow.

The sparkling blue pond—
So calm,
So still,
So untouched—
Tells me it's time to go.

The golden sun sets,
Leaving a cloudy pink sky.
With time passing,
I sit back,
Inhale,
And cry,
Wishing for happiness,
Praying for the future,
Forgetting the past,
Wanting nature to last.

The Beach of My Childhood
Jean Legge Hiscock

The beach of my childhood is still there, sandwiched between craggy cliffs that separate it from the once gut-and-bone-strewn beach where the fishermen cleaned their catch. Only a faint stench can reach this far, and, diluted by a refreshing breeze from the sea, it is not altogether unpleasant.

As children, we often played here, where the pebbles have been rounded and stained white by the action and salt of the waves. How happy we were, singing and bathing, playing mothers and babes. All of us were dressed only in bloomers, but none of us felt the least bit self-conscious. None of us had ever seen a bathing suit, except in Eaton's catalogue, and we could only dream of some day owning one.

We dashed about like mice, over the hard rocks, our feet sinking and sliding among the pebbles and sand, heedless of the cool breeze blowing from the glittering Arctic ice in the bay. We hardly noticed the slubby rocks covered with golden brown kelp—kelp that bobbed and twirled in the waves like flowers and grass in the wind—in which ugly tarnished orange crabs hid with their neighbours, black tansies, like miniature snakes.

Intent on trying to catch lumpfish the size of a thumbnail that swam among the sea lice in the crevices of the cliffs, we were oblivious to the sound of ivory seagulls screeching overhead. They circled and dipped, scavengers of the sea plucking out bright orange squid and silvery green caplin, all the while screaming the cries of a thousand weeping women.

True sea urchins, we dashed in and out of the chilly water to our fancy. Unmindful of the cold, we stood with the sand and debris washing our feet and scraping our tanned-brown legs.

Perhaps then the fog would roll in, obscuring our vision, and we would don our clothes to rid our skin of its clammy dampness.

All of us knew the thrill of scaling the steep treacherous banks, of searching for the rare and coveted fish teeth— so white and shiny—and of finding the weathered conk shells with the sound of the sea trapped inside them. We sometimes sat on the pebbly shore, scaling the sun-baked sand off our goose-pimply legs.

My friends and I felt the spray of the waves that dashed and chased each other like us children. We didn't often watch the waves splash against the rugged black and red cliffs with a gentle thud or, when there was a storm of wind, come crashing in like rampaging savages, kicking the rocks and spraying the beach with a deafening roar.

Instead, on a hot sunny day, we would lie on the flat hot cliffs, lick the brine off our lips and stare into the brilliant blue sky, where soft white clouds drifted like a multitude of angels spreading their wings to protect us from unknown dangers.

Bodies and Bones:

Saying Goodbye Forever

Untitled
Danyelle Lavers

Turn around and look outside
Stare into the devil's eyes
Your brain is numb
Your skin is loose
Put your head into the noose.

I see the fire;
It is inside of me;
It will burn all
Of my feelings
And desires.

I will no longer
Feel nor fear
The pain this world
Presents me with,
'Cause this world
Is filled with emptiness and nothing more.

Completion
D. Jean Young

In a corner of a certain university biology lab, there is a skeleton. It wears a brass name tag: TWYLA BROWN. Sometimes, a wandering sunbeam bounces off this tag. After class, a student stays. She reads the name and wonders who this skeleton used to be. She wonders why these bones hang from the gleaming metal hook . . . .

Twyla Brown smoked her last cigarette. She inhaled deeply, savouring the gentle, nicotine high. There. The Export A Light pack was empty. She sniffed the lingering tobacco smell on the foil inside the golden pack, crumpled the foil into a ball, aimed, and threw it into the pink plastic wastepaper basket by her dresser. She tossed the pack in, too. There was nothing else in the clean basket. She'd spent two hours scrubbing her rented room. No one was going to say that she had left a mess.

Twyla sat on a wooden chair that was missing a rung, turned on the lights of her make-up mirror. She drummed her fingers, debated whether she should bother. Ah, she decided, I might as well. Even if it washes off. The commercials say this stuff's waterproof. I'll give it the torture test. My freckles are showing through the foundation. Always do. Can't expect miracles.

Twyla lined her eyes carefully, heavily; added extra coats of mascara and moss-green shadow; added bronze blush to her cheekbones; brushed on a coppery lipstick. The end result was a bit overdone. But if it ran, she'd never know. She chewed on the handle of her blush brush, decided to do her thick, rusty-red hair in a French

49

braid. That style stayed in and looked neat.

Too bad she didn't have a full-length mirror in her room. She'd peep into Mrs. Bryant's bedroom on her way down the hall. Mrs. Bryant's closet doors were mirrored.

What should she wear? Twyla played around with that question. She had on her best underwear: lacy bra and matching panties. Dear as diamond dust, if she'd paid for the set. Easy to sneak it under the plain clothes snoop's nose. Stupid, putting a guy on lingerie. All she had to do was ask him what size bra he thought she took; he'd turned red and ran. She grinned at the memory.

She folded her fluffy, royal blue housecoat, packed it away in her suitcase. She picked out a pair of tight-fitting black jeans, an ivory turtleneck, a black, hand-knit sweater embroidered with fake pearls. She snapped the suitcase closed, put it by the door. It stood by neat stacks of paperbacks, marked with a note on pink notepaper: "PLEASE GIVE TO THE HOSPITAL."

She'd like to go out in a long, elegant, black silk skirt; high heels; a high-buttoned white blouse; oodles of golden chains. If she'd owned any of that stuff. Ah, she decided, I'm too short and top-heavy for that rig to work. Twyla packed her make-up away, used a tissue to wipe up some stray powder. She stretched and shook her body loose. Next, she folded two notes into pretty pink envelopes selected for this special occasion.

"Freeman, come here," she called. Her landlady's ten-year-old son came to her door hopefully. Twyla paid him to do errands sometimes. He'd do anything for a loonie. She gave him two five dollar bills and very specific delivery orders. "There's another five if you get it just right," she promised. When Freeman left, Twyla folded a five into another envelope. She wrote his name on it and left it on her dresser.

Creep Number One and his wife should get their notes within five minutes of each other. If Freeman timed it right, there'd be no trouble finding the body. Twyla felt sure that one, if not both of them, would act on the note. She was counting on that.

Now, it was all settled. Funny how she was feeling outside of it all now. Like she was watching herself, feeling calm and easy, kind of tired.

She called a taxi, telling the dispatcher when she'd want the ride. "Get the time right, George, or I'll call the competition."

"Sure, Twyla. We knows what you're like."

She had some time before the taxi came. She plumped her flat pillow, stretched out on her bed, closed her eyes. All week, in between making plans, she'd been doing this. Going back, little by little. She was ready now to go back right to the first. To the thing that stuck when she started to know who she was.

"Welfare bums!" The woman in a clean white blouse and black pants turned to her friend and pointed as they passed by Twyla and her parents. Her friend nodded agreement.

Twyla looked up from her mud pie. She didn't know what the words meant. But she clenched her tiny fists and ran to her parents. They sat in cheap lawn chairs with an open cardboard case of beer between them.

"We're not welfare bums, we're not!" cried Twyla. "Are we?"

"Shh, shh," said her mother. She poured red Kool-Aid for her daughter. Her hands shook. She spilled some.

51

Her real mother had a warm lap, cuddling arms. She smelled like beer. Twyla never forgot her. Never forgot who her real mother was. Not when the social worker took her to a foster home where the new "mother" talked to others about "my welfare kid." Not when they gave her nice clothes, her own bed; not when they told her, "You'll turn out bad; your kind always does."

Sometimes, tired of failing, Twyla tried to prove the "mother" wrong. Once, she'd worked hard to bring home a report card lettered with A's, while the "mother's" son had C's and D's.

"They picks on you," the "mother" said to her son. And to Twyla she said, "So, I s'pose you thinks you're really something, now. Well, if you're so smart, how come you're not rich?" Then she'd laugh her ugly laugh. Twyla didn't want to beat the son next time.

After high school was finally over, Twyla moved out on her own. She'd planned to prove them all wrong. She babysat, got jobs pumping gas, packing groceries. She lost jobs. Because . . . everyone picked on me, she told herself; then she shook her head. No, might as well admit the truth. The time for lying was past. She'd lost her jobs because she'd told off her bosses, because she'd never charged her friends for gas, because she'd undercharged the poor for groceries (why should they have to pay as much as the rich ones?). She'd never hurt anyone she liked; she'd never helped anyone she couldn't stand. Sooner or later, she always lost her job. Maybe the "mother" was right—badness must have been born in her.

Twyla looked at her Timex. Her taxi wasn't due for another half-hour. She took a crossword puzzle book from the shelf over her bed. There was one puzzle not quite finished. She hated anything half done. All or nothing. That's the way things should be. Be the best or be the worst. She filled in the answers in ink, quickly. They were too easy, now that she'd done the others.

Like everything. Too hard or too easy. Life didn't make sense. Maybe death was crazy, too. She'd take the chance. Maybe she'd burn in Hell. So what?

She had memorized the Ten Commandments one Sunday School year. The "mother" had sent her there every week. On a big yellow school bus crowded with noisy kids.

If suicide is a mortal sin, she thought, I'll go to Hell. Do I deserve to go to Hell, I wonder? Let's see now. Let's check. They says the whole Bible is based on the Ten Commandments. If I broke them all, well, then it's off to Hell I go. It's the right place for me. Might even make a few friends there. Meet some old ones. What's the order of them? Ah, it doesn't matter—I'll count the ten.

"Thou shalt not worship false images." Twyla's Sunday School teacher had said in her squeaky voice through her buck teeth. "That's what Catholics do with statues."

I didn't want to be like her, like them, Twyla reflected. She grinned as she remembered how she'd sneaked into the unlocked Catholic church on winter afternoons, staying there until darkness scared her home. A kind-looking statue of Mary looked down at her as she chatted. Mary never answered. But she always listened.

"Where you been?" the "mother" would ask.
"Out."
"Out where?"
"Around."

The "mother" would roll her eyes. At supper, she'd tell her husband, "We're going to have to start watching the welfare kid; she's headed for trouble."

One day, the son had tailed Twyla. After she'd bent to tie her boot lace, she looked around. She saw him, peering from behind a tree. She never again went to talk to Mary. He wasn't going to spoil that.

"Thou shalt have no other gods before me." Why not, she wondered. Maybe I'll reincarnate . . . if I don't go to Hell. Or maybe, I'll go on and on 'til I reach Nirvana. Learning about that stuff was the best part of high school religion. Maybe there were other gods. Maybe they were better.

"Thou shalt not covet." Hah! No, boy. Don't want what the other guy's got. Like there's anyone that good. Pictures, like clips from a video, flashed through her mind. A mother and child playing on a beach. A silver fox fur. A plain, gold wedding band, worn with tiny scratches. She'd coveted all her life.

"Thou shalt not steal." Other kids had money for chocolate bars. Big shots drove Cadillacs. They didn't have to steal. These commandments sounded like they were made by some rich, comfortable guy who didn't want for nothing.

"Remember the Sabbath and keep it holy." Sure. Keep the only day she had off holy. No. She smiled, remembering Sundays. Parties, work, adultery and not too much church, thank you.

"Honour thy father and thy mother." Who? Why? She clenched her teeth, fought against another almost-forgotten memory. The feel of being flung across a kitchen, crying, "Don't hurt Mommy, Daddy! Don't!"; she remembered the sting of the black leather belt across her arms, and the look of the hurting, red, puffy mark.

"Thou shalt not bear false witness against thy neighbour." Sometimes, she decided, it's the decent thing to do. I'm glad I helped put Lenny in jail. Glad I planted that load of crack in his car. I sat there in court, dressed neat and respectable. Swore on the Bible. Said he was a dealer. Said I bought from him all the time. He's in jail now. Locked up. For five years. He wouldn't be in that long for beating Julie. You don't get much for slapping your wife around. I'm glad I was a false witness. Glad!

Twyla flopped on her lumpy bed one last time. She checked her braid—still nice and tight. Those clothes were not going to wrinkle. In ten minutes, the taxi would be there.

"Thou shalt not take the Lord's name in vain." She smiled. Every day almost, until she was fourteen and in love with a quiet boy, she'd cursed. Probably the first words she knew.

"I don't want my girl talking like that. It's gross," he'd said.

Loving him, she'd stopped cursing. When he went on to other girls, she never took up cursing again. Not ever. All or nothing.

"Thou shalt not commit adultery." Now, that was a good one, too. John (tall, strong, flat stomach, nice bum), Mike (a runt, liked it fast, good), Sam (he brought roses and wine), and Kerry (sweet, truly guilty about his wife, sweet Kerry), some of her best lovers: all married. The best ones always were. She knew the score, knew they'd stick with their wives. As long as that was clear, it was okay.

But Creep Number One, he'd led her on, said he loved her. I was fool enough to believe him, she thought. Made a mistake there. Found that out all right the last time we were together. Let myself go, let myself trust. Never done that before.

He was putting on his pants when he'd said, "I love you. I'll always love you." Had given her this warm glow. Till he'd put his other leg in. "But I can't leave my poor wife. She's not strong like you. She'd fall apart." Bastard had just enough decency to turn red when he'd said that; wouldn't look at me, though.

I'm all alone again. That's the first thing Twyla had thought. And then, he's alone, too, but he don't know it. The fool. The weak, pitiful fool. All her love and all her wanting just floated away. All or nothing. He'd been nothing to her after that.

Keeps calling me, she mused. Over and over. He'll do something when he gets my note. Or his wife will. I s'pose someone will do something. Someone will come around to drag my body out before the current tows me off for good. Might not though. She chewed her thumb nail. Might never ever be found. Smelt would have a good feed. Don't have to do this. Don't have to. It's not too late. Not yet.

Twyla stood up, straightened out the bedspread. She put her board money, with enough for an extra week, into another pink envelope for Mrs. Bryant. She tucked it in with her Last Will and Testament.

"Give all of my clothes to the Salvation Army," she'd written.

Medical science and the donor bank could have her body. If it was worth anything. If the fish didn't get it first.

"Please put a name tag on my bones." Would they listen? Would they bother?

No need for a funeral. She didn't want no welfare coffin, and Mrs. Bryant might feel like she had to do something.

She licked the envelope, thinking as the glue stuck to her tongue. Will my skeleton hang in a classroom? Might get to go to university after all. Will I know when they boil the meat from my bones? Leon, my sweet little art student, says I got "good bones." Might as well show them off instead of letting them rot underground. Nice and quick, boiling's going to be, not rotting away little by little with worms crawling in my eyeballs.

She touched the soft skin of her cheek. Funny to think of it all being gone in a little while.

Twyla looked at her watch, touched the cold window. Frosty, fancy ferns. Pretty. Cold. Heat from her finger melted a black circle. Left a mark like a hole in an almost frozen pond.

Too cold to wait outside long. She'd go to Hell (where it was warm) in style. She'd get a ride. Right to the bridge. The taxi would be there soon. Twyla pulled on her bike-style leather jacket. It fit just right. Worn right into her shape. She put on her black felt derby. Best hat she liked. Paid for it at the Salvation Army Thrift Store. Good stuff there sometimes. She'd brightened it up by adding neon green ribbon around the band and two long feathers from the fly-tying section of K-Mart. Never paid for the trimmings.

The taxi horn blared through the walls. She quickly checked her looks in Mrs. Bryant's full-length mirror, then she went out the back door, through the kitchen. Mrs.

Bryant was drying the supper dishes. She was a good soul.

Twyla stopped for a second. "Thanks for everything," she said. Impulsively, she kissed the older woman. Felt right to do that just then. Mrs. Bryant gave her a puzzled smile. She patted her cheek where Twyla's lips had touched her.

Mrs. Bryant had put up with Twyla through three lost jobs and who knows how many lovers. She wouldn't let anyone say a bad word about Twyla. She'd feel bad when she heard the news. But then, she'd get another boarder, raise the rent. Probably she was losing now. Didn't charge enough.

She didn't know about the ad. Twyla had paid for it, told them to run it next week. It advertised "Reasonable board for construction worker." A man wouldn't care who'd been in a room before him.

The taxi horn bleated again. Twyla gave Mrs. Bryant a quick smile. Geez. Her throat felt all swelled up now. She pulled on her leather gloves. "Gotta go now." Then she was running down the concrete walkway. The cold made her nostrils stick together.

Eddie Rogers, a guy from her high school, tapped the steering wheel of the taxi. She sat in the front seat so they could chat. "Take me to the Legion," she ordered. She didn't want him to start asking questions.

"Taxiing gives me a bit of extra money," Eddie said. "I'm not reporting it on my pogey."

"Wouldn't blame you. They'd fool up your cheques for weeks."

"Some cold."

"Yeah. Freezing."

Eddie stopped in the Legion parking lot. Twyla stayed in her seat. Music pounded through the walls. The Legion door opened and grey clouds of heated air poured into the cold. Might be someone in there fit to love. Might be. She could look for a job on Monday. Or fill out an application to go to school. She could go inside, scrap all her plans. Spend the last of her money. Every cent.

She might even find another lousy relationship. She couldn't have a baby. Pelvic Inflammatory Disease, from the coil, the doctor had said. Could keep on going, doing reruns.

No. What's the sense of that? More misery. That's all. She leaned back, closed her eyes. Making up her mind for sure now. Making sure everything was all set. All done. There was something poking at her mind, like she'd forgotten something.

It hit her then. It was that last commandment. "Thou shalt not kill." That one's not broke. Not yet. So, did that mean a trip up on the way to Hell? A time hanging around in that awful place the Catholics called Limbo? Just hanging there? Like this? Like now? Better to burn. To feel something.

She played with the thought while the dispatcher asked Eddie if he could pick up another fare.

"Not yet," Eddie answered. "Still waiting on Twyla. We're here at the Legion."

"Tell her to make up her mind, Eddie. Hope you got the meter running."

"Shut up, George. I'll call in when I'm ready." He put the speaker back on the hook. "Well, Twyla, what now? Are you going in there or are you going somewhere else?"

"Somewhere else." Her voice was soft, husky. It was

all clear now. She didn't care enough to kill anyone else. Not enough to rot in jail. Not enough to make plans. Didn't even hate the "mother" enough for that. But there was herself, sure. And it was all set now. All she had to do was fill in the last square. Suicide was killing. Then it was all done. Nice and neat.

"Eddie," her voice was stronger now, "take me to the Bridge. I'm meeting someone there."

"That's a queer place to meet someone. Sure you want to go there?"

"I'm sure. Come on. Let's go. Don't want to be late."

Eddie shrugged and started driving. It wasn't far. He said, "I'll wait with you till he comes. Too cold to leave you standing out there."

"No! He don't want anyone to see him with me." They'd reached the Bridge. Eddie pulled over to the side.

"I'll wait. I can keep my mouth shut. The stories I could tell you . . . ."

"Get lost, Eddie. Told you, we want to be alone. He'll be here in a minute. He'd have a fit if he thought anyone knew about us." She gave him a fifty-dollar bill. Her last bit of money. She'd kept it till now. Just in case she changed her mind. Just in case.

"Just a sec, now; I'll give you your change."

"Keep it. You can use it more than me."

"Don't be silly. No wonder you're always broke, Twyla. Now take your change."

"No. Now scram, Eddie. Get lost. I told you, he doesn't want anyone to see him.

"Yes, Boss. I'll check back later. Just to make sure you don't freeze to death."

"Don't you dare."

Eddie drove away. She saw him check his rear-view mirror twice. She waved good-bye. He went 'round a turn. He couldn't see her now. Their little spat left her feeling good.

There wasn't a car in sight. Twyla checked her watch. Timing was just about right. She hummed as she carefully climbed atop the concrete rail. Might as well do it right.

Tricky, this is, she thought. Those boots aren't made for walking on rails. There. She was all set. Steady as a rock. Not a breeze. All right, too—cold enough as it was. Face was numb already. She made sure she knew where her feet were before she looked down at the cold, black water. Even in the dark, she could make out the swirl around the concrete pillars. Almost hypnotizing, like it was calling her now, saying hurry up, hurry up!

Twyla took a deep breath. The cold hurt her chest. Might as well try to end it with style. She pretended to be an Olympic diver. Stood up like they did on TV. "It's all in the focus," one had said. "You have to see how you're going to fall."

She saw a straight dive, nothing fancy, like an arrow or a lead weight going down in one clean move.

It was her first dive. Still, she hit the water just like she'd imagined. Down she went; down, down, down; farther than she'd thought she could. Maybe, she thought, this is the straight way to Hell. The sudden shock wore off; the cold grabbed onto her. Her body took over then, made her struggle to get the air it needed. Gasping, she bobbed to the top.

Icy water cut through her jeans, seeped up under her jacket, shivered up her back. Filled her boots. She was trying not to sink now. Wishing she'd learned to swim so she could head for shore. Hard to breathe. Gasping like a weeping kid.

Then she saw the headlights overhead, saw them stop on the bridge. Damn body! Didn't want to die. Well, she'd show it. They weren't going to haul her out of this looking like a drowned rat. The "mother" would say she couldn't even do that right. No. Had to stop that flailing. Stop the fighting.

Shouldn't be too hard. Boots like lead. Dragging down. All I got to do, she told herself, is let it all go. That's all. Stay still. Lie back and take it. Let myself go all limp— the way a man likes a woman to do sometimes—and I'll sink, I'll sink, right to the bottom. Can do that. Stay still. Let myself turn into nothing. There now. It's working. Not even shaking now. Ooh. The water's in my nose, my mouth, my ears. That's why I can't swim. Hated getting water in my nose. Wait now. Stop thinking. That's the way.

She started clawing to the top again. Her body had its own mind. But the water was winning now. It wasn't up to her anymore. Not up to her at all.

She's going numb, doesn't want to fight, seeing red. Hell? Don't matter. Nothing matters. Not afraid now. Can't change the darkness.

She grabs her knees, curls up. Like a baby in its womb. Nice now, floating in the darkness, just fl . . . .

In a corner of a certain university biology lab, there is a skeleton. It wears a brass name tag: TWYLA BROWN. Sometimes, a wandering sunbeam bounces off this tag. After class, a student stays. She reads the name and wonders who this skeleton used to be. She wonders why these bones hang from the gleaming metal hook.

Dark House in Which I Stand
Billy Parsons

Dark house, by which once more I stand,
An eerie feeling seeping down my spine;
The sky lightening with a blast,
The ground a'bubbling, will not last.

My breath spilling from my lungs,
Me a'running rump-a-pum,
The ground drowning in the mud,
Me a'sucking down with blood.

Air refilling my limp body,
Propelling me into life.

The cat-like eyes in the sky
Pierce my soul. Will I die?
But I don't, and still I run;
I sink into the ground—
All that's left, a thumb.

Demons fade and fuzz through my mind;
Still I last and ask, "Why?";
I then enter the dark house;
Is my heart a'pounding? I don't know.

Inside this house,
Every horror of life
Attacks me.

Do You Remember Sara?
Jean Legge Hiscock

Have you heard about Sara? Do you remember the night she returned to our house screaming? "They're going to get me!" she cried frantically, still banging on the door even as I held it open. You put your arms around her, led her to a chair and tried to comfort her as I made tea. Poor Sara. You and I knew there was no one after her, didn't we?

They found her last night, her body battered and raped. She never should have left. I begged her not to, but she didn't want to impose on our hospitality any longer. I think she sensed that you didn't want her here, that it grated on your nerves the way she combed her hair and smoked at the kitchen table, leaving long hairs and ashes about. I could see that it bothered you when she went about the house in her flimsy nightgowns.

You were glad she left. You said it was costing us a fortune to keep her here. I know the grocery bill went up a hundred dollars the month that she lived here, but it was worth it to me to have someone help tidy up and get supper ready when I came home from work. You always spend your days in the woods, hunting and fishing, and then you complain when I don't get the evening meal on the table fast enough—I know you like to eat and then take a nap in the recliner as you watch the news.

It should be on the news tonight. The police haven't released many details yet. Poor Sara. Some people called her a bastard, but it wasn't her fault she had a slut for a mother and no one knew who her father was. She was beautiful, and smart, too. She worked hard in school and did well and could have made something of herself if only she could have gotten the money for college.

We talked a lot at work, she and I. She was a damn good waitress, but then she left. She said she got pinched on the behind too many times, and all them truckers didn't tip much—although most of them wanted her to go to bed with them.

You have to admit it: if you were twenty years younger, you'd have gone after her yourself. I could see it in your eyes. Admit it. You were glad she left.

She went to the mainland and sent us a card at Christmas with a little note scribbled on it. She said she was lonely and didn't like big city life and the rent was too high. I didn't know she came back. Not 'til this morning, when I heard about it on the news.

Will you come to the funeral with me? The suit you bought to be buried in is all pressed up in the closet with a garbage bag over it. It won't hurt to wear it once. It would mean a lot to me.

Even though you didn't like her much, she trusted us. That's why she came to our door. You remember the night—why, you'd just gotten home yourself.

Come to think of it, where were you that night?

To an Unfaithful Spouse
Jean Legge Hiscock

Oh, skeleton, rest in your grave,
your lofty soul is fled.
You're just a feast for the worms now,
you're Dead, Dead, Dead.

You can't hear the trees now,
as they whisper in the wind.
Or the singing of the birds now,
and you won't, again.

Oh, the clothes, the jewels you had—
money could buy no more.
You wined and dined and lived a lot,
but now it's o'er.

Your golden hair is matted now,
and God, what a smell.
I wish you could see yourself now,
but you can't—in Hell.

You thought you could trick me—
you bedded another man!
You can't have any fun, now,
but I will, I can.

Oh, what a daft, great fool you were;
how easy you were led.
I'm standing here and laughing,
and you're Dead, Dead, Dead.

A Deadly Reply
Jean Legge Hiscock

Come join me in this coffin, dear,
I swear it was made for two;
These bones don't need a lot of space,
there's lots of room for you!

You always were a puny man,
and really not that tall.
Effeminate, I think you call it;
perhaps that's why you're small.

My golden hair needs washing,
and never mind the smell.
I may stink a little in my grave,
but you stank on earth as well.

I know you've always hated cats,
but I had jewels and money.
Too bad my Bootsie got it all,
though you were slick and cunning.

What fun it was haunt you,
and drive you to your death.
But Hell goes on forever,
so it's not over yet!

The Extermination of a Rat
Jean Legge Hiscock

Jenny had little recollection of her early childhood. The only vivid memory was that of when she was a child of about five or six. She remembered sitting, wailing ceaselessly, on an outdoor platform one mid-morning. An old great uncle happened along.

"Why do you cry so often, child," he had asked, "and for such a long time?"

The child, with her fists balled and pushing against her eyeballs, stopped the incessant crying for a moment and pondered the uncle's question. True, Uncle didn't know what she had to cry about, but the pain from last night was gone now and today was bright and sunny. The tears dried on her dirt-streaked face.

After that, the child was seen to be more normal, almost as normal as her little playmates.

She gloried in performing sadistic acts on them. She would sit behind an unsuspecting child at school and push the point of her pencil into his neck until the top broke off and stayed there. She might get into a fight with another child and tear off her coat, toss it into the mud, and trample it, making sure that it was ruined. Her twisted little mind was forever thinking up new evils to give her an inward sense of satisfaction.

In school, Jenny did not perform well. In the first grade, she was completely disoriented. She was a total failure.

Hoping to be rid of her next year, the teacher moved Jenny ahead to second grade.

There Jenny continued to be as much a failure as ever. A new subject was introduced in grade two:

Spelling. Each day, Teacher would call out the words for the children to spell. Each day, Jenny went to the front of the class to receive her two straps on each hand for misspelling the words. No one ever saw her cry in school. Indeed, she always returned to her seat with a smirk on her face. Every day was always as the day before, until the new teacher came.

He was considered a sissy—a *man* teaching grades one and two. On this particular day, the lesson was arithmetic. Jenny painstakingly copied the sums from the blackboard. She filled in the blanks with whatever numbers popped into her head. Occasionally, she was lucky and came up with the right answer; most often, she was wrong.

Then one day, her teacher, in his soft, effeminate voice said, "Jenny, you have to pay attention. Listen to what I say."

Jenny was surprised. In her little girl's mind, she thought, "Listen: to pay attention is to 'listen' to him talk."

From that day onward, there was a marked improvement in the child. Indeed, she went from appearing retarded to seeming bright. She brought home good reports, but she was never cheery.

Her small, thin face always wore a thoughtful expression. She still seemed to take extreme pleasure in the pain of her peers. If a friend fell on the ice, she slyly gave him a gentle push, just so the bruised knee would be sure to jar on an upraised stump. These acts of cruelty were seldom noted although they continued all through Jenny's childhood.

She was thirteen on the day her Mama sent her to the cellar to fetch potatoes for supper. Jenny heard a quick, scurrying noise. She glanced quickly up at the rat poison on the shelf—two boxes of it—enough to . . . . Jenny tried to take hold of her thoughts, to control herself, but one thought smothered all the others. She'd bake a molasses cake for her father. He could take it with him when he went wood-cutting. Trembling, she almost forgot the potatoes she'd come for. She hurried to the potato bin and quickly filled her bowl.

That night when he came to her bed, Jenny quietly gritted her teeth, squeezed her eyes shut as he took her, fondling her breasts; all the while, he kept up a steady rhythm until at last, with a loud grunt, he was done with her. Quietly, he left her room and crept back to her mother.

"I'll bake you your cake tomorrow," thought Jenny, filled with a hatred too big for her small body to contain. The sun was creeping over the horizon before sleep finally stole over her once more.

Papa had left for the woods when Jenny awoke.

"Did you hear the rats last night, Mama?" Jenny asked as she stoked up the fire to heat the oven.

"Well, I might'a heard something, Jenny," said Mama, intent on her task of kneading the dough in the bread pan. "I sleeps sound. I noticed some of the potatoes got holes in them, and the turnips is half-eat. Your father got some rat poison last week. He never got a chance to spread it around yet."

"I'll spread some around this morning," said Jenny. "You never knows, I might even catch the biggest rat."

"Never mind the talk about them rats, child. You said you was going to bake your father a molasses cake to take in the woods tomorrow. Now hurry on down to the cellar and fetch the molasses."

"Yes, Mama," said Jenny obediently. She took the measuring jug and a large bowl to the cellar. As she descended the ladder, the arthritis in her left leg warned of the advent of damp weather. She hoped her father would get at least one more day in the woods before the rain came.

Luck was with her. The next morning dawned bright and clear. Papa rose early. Being the greedy man that he was, he took the whole cake with him. Jenny listened as he left; then, she rolled over in her bed for a peaceful nap.

The weather a few days later was foggy and wet. A sharp northeast wind whistled in the trees. It was cold out on the point in the graveyard. Jenny hunched further down into her coat.

The preacher spoke fast, hurrying through the service, anxious to return to the warmth of his kitchen. Whimpering women and husky-voiced men gathered round Jenny and her mother and said how sad that a young man like her father—with so much to live for—should die so suddenly.

No one thought to question the girl. In so remote a village as theirs, murder was an unthought-of crime. The nearest law enforcement officer was a month away by dog sled in winter, three weeks away by boat when the harbour was clear of ice. No medical doctor came this way, though every six months or so, a nurse came to stock the general store's shelves with cough concoctions and the like.

To some, it seemed strange that the child shed not a tear. There were whisperings that the full impact of her father's death had not hit her yet, and, they said, how hard it would be when the truth did set in!

Jenny lingered in the graveyard as the grave diggers lowered the rough wooden box. She kicked the first dirt onto the coffin, then turned and fled.

A Bit of This, A Bit of That:

Making Cabbitt Stew

Fine Material
Billy Parsons

Satin gown of fine material—
Beauty it has embraced—
The purest cotton lining
Covered in velvet lace.

Worn by queens and such,
Created by the best,
Every gem held in gold
And encrusted in its vest.

And then, one day, it was tossed—
Into the dump it fell,
Followed by a garbage truck;
It was dragged away to hell.

Soon, covered in morning dew,
The wind blew,
Launching it into orbit,
A flowing, glowing red hue.

It covered streets,
Its future very hazy;
Then, it landed
By a homeless old lady.

The Next Mr. Olympia
David Elliot

Ah! The gym. The place where muscles are molded and men are made, where a person can enter as a pathetic and paltry representative of the human race and emerge, like the caterpillar from its cocoon, an enviable specimen of form and grace. So I thought.

My inspiration to shape up happened one day as I was thumbing through a health magazine which my wife, Diane, had bought. A full-page ad for a particular brand of health food, guaranteed to cure every ailment from hair loss to painful foot bunions, caught my eye. However, it wasn't the food that sparked my interest as much as it was the two people in the picture. One was a muscular fellow, a souped-up bionic man who sat on a stool, his white teeth glistening through an effortless smile as he curled a 90-pound weight with his left arm. His bulging muscles made him look like Mr. Olympia times two.

Standing next to this block of carved marble was a woman. But not just any woman. No, sir. This female was the epitome of physical perfection, the one a man begins dreaming about as soon as his hormones start pumping and about whom he continues to dream until his heart stops pumping. As she looked out from the page smiling at me, I felt a sudden urge to pump up, to become a specimen worthy of note. Furthermore, I reasoned, my wife would be proud of the new super-developed Dave I was beginning to envision.

"Diane, I'm joining the local fitness club," I said, putting down the magazine.

"Why?"

"To work out."

"Why?"

"To develop my physique."

"Why?"

"So I'll look better."

"Why?"

I had a gut feeling that this wasn't going anywhere, especially when she asked me about my back, which always acted up when there were things to do like shovel snow, mow the lawn, or change the cat litter. I went to the basement and found my gym bag with John, Paul, George and Ringo embossed on the side, smiling innocently. With a "humph!", I headed for the club. "After a couple of sessions, she'll change her mind," I muttered.

As I entered the sanctuary of iron and machismo, the first thing I saw was a guy posing in front of one of the full length mirrors that surrounded the place. As he tensed himself, every muscle in his body popped out, each looking like it was after the "Lump of the Year" award. His bulging veins and rippled form resembled a topographic map complete with three-dimensional relief features.

Now, I didn't think for one second that I could compare with this chunk of human granite, but, like many men who go through mid-life crises thinking silly things, I thought I was in reasonable shape. I took off my shirt and, standing next to Atlas, flexed. Nothing. A couple of well-formed females smiled sympathetically.

I decided to walk around to get some idea of what people did in these places. I watched as guys strained and creaked under tremendous weight loads and as they encouraged each other to do "just one more." I noticed that some weight-lifting zealots who push themselves to their limit and beyond often grunt and groan a lot, yell and scream and curse, and, from time to time, emit funny smells.

After my survey, I decided to begin my journey into this brave new world of form and fitness with a warm-up on an exercise bike. I sat next to one of the young women who had smiled at me. She had her machine set on a difficulty level of seven for a time interval of six minutes. I smiled disparagingly at her small frame and set my bike on the maximum tension level of twelve for ten minutes. *When she sees what I'm capable of doing,* I thought, *she'll giggle on the other side of her face.* I began to pedal vigorously.

Within thirty seconds I knew I was in trouble. My lungs had started to burn and my heart had approached the beat of a drum roll. My legs ached, my eyes watered, my nose ran. "Keep going," urged a little voice inside me. "You'll get your second wind before you know it."

Freshly inspired by this thought, I leaned into the handle bars, gritted my teeth, and pedalled harder. After what felt like forever, my legs went from ache to numb, my arms and groin had knotted, and I wanted to throw up. Sweat soaked my shirt and matted my thinning hair to my scalp. My sinuses drained. The wax melted in my ears. My breathing sounded like a coffee machine gasping and sputtering through its morning brewing cycle. I checked the elapsed-time display. Fifty-five seconds.

At this point, another little voice told me my second wind was busy elsewhere and that the best thing for me to do was stop. I obeyed, stepped off the bike, and crashed headlong onto a floor mat. A surge of panic shot through me until I noticed my legs were still attached. I forced myself up, wobbled to a post, and hugged it dearly, making a forty-five degree angle with the floor.

"Are you okay?" a distant-sounding voice asked.

"I . . . I think so," I wheezed.

"Your first time here, right?"

"Yes," I gasped. No point trying to bluff.

"My name is Bruno. When you get your breath, I'll set you up with a proper routine."

"Thanks," I croaked, as my vision cleared enough for me to see an inverted triangle on sawlog-sized legs.

After twenty minutes, I had recovered sufficiently to approach Bruno, who gave me a fitness test to see what level of program I should start at. The results showed pre-beginner, an ego-deflating conclusion which I normally would have disputed, but as Bruno looked down on me with a what-are-you-going-to-do-about-it stare, I acquiesced.

As I worked my routine, I wandered near a bunch of Superman-type fellows who were totally focused on their training. I wanted to befriend some of these pieces of molded concrete, so I waited for my chance to interject a little levity into their conversation. After all, humour has often proved itself to be an effective ice-breaker.

"What are you working on today?" one muscular brute asked of another.

"Legs," came the reply.

"And you?"

"Arms," responded another.

Here was my opportunity. "Hey, guys!" I said excitedly, "I can't wait to get home for supper!"

"Why?" someone dared to ask.

"So I can work on jaws!" I shot back, waiting for the din of uncontrollable laughter to reverberate throughout the gym, bouncing off mirrors, mats and assorted dumbbells. My effort, however, received silence, cold stares, and some hand gestures I hadn't seen in a long time.

In the interest of good health and longevity, I slunk away from this unappreciative bunch of muscular bipeds and continued to work my way through the routine I had been given. I exercised upper body parts, lower body parts, inner body parts, outer body parts, private body parts, and body parts that are not found in any human anatomy book. I finished the program in just under two hours, a feat I felt pleased with until Bruno told me that it should have taken thirty minutes.

The next morning, as I applied some Deep Heat rub to several areas that were screaming for relief, I saw the health food ad from the day before. To show my fantasy female how I had improved with my first session at the gym, I stood before the mirror, ignored the stiffness and soreness, and flexed my chest muscles. Nothing.

"That's okay, sweetheart, give me a little time," I said, as she continued smiling at me.

Or was she laughing?

A Woodcutter Reflects While Dancing

Vincent Colin Burke

Whence do they come,
Those footsteps light
That mingle now with mine?
Where will they go, that knot behind,
Which I tie now by turning?
My hand on yours is rough,
You say—
'Tis natural:
The tree, being bitten, will
Protect its bark;
Your fingertips, however, are calloused
At the roots,
From tapping tidy type across
The blanched and battered face
Of tree you never knew.
But I slay friends to keep you warm,
Or such as you,
And I must say for them that it
Is worth the loss of life—
Or it were suicide and murder.
With music ending, return now
To your friends,
To walking paths unblended—
What did you say? I
Dance well,
Do I?
I hadn't known it—
Thank you.

Lonely Dinky
Daphne Russell

I am your dinky; come play with me.
I was left in your stocking, by the chimney.
You ate all your goodies and tossed me aside.
You won't play with me, so now I must hide.

You play with your wagon and your big Tonka truck.
Your big toys you liked more, that's just my luck.
If Santa had left me under your tree,
Who would you have loved better, would I still be
lonely?

I can fit in your pocket; I can fit in your hand;
I can fit in your book bag, or in your lunch can.
But you won't play with me; I am sad, don't you see?
I will hide here forever; no one will find me.

When you are grown up and have your own car,
Treat it with kindness, drive it with care.
It can be dangerous, please listen to me.
I will always love you, your lonely dinky.

Screeched In
Nellie P. Strowbridge

Page One writers were left holding Nino Ricci's bags
after his Canada Council Reading weekend
of The Newfoundland & Labrador Writers' Alliance.
East coast writers had scattered . . . .

Nino Ricci went quietly to his fate
on a Sunday afternoon in Deer Lake,
his dark eyes as mysterious to his female captors
as this strange rite was to him . . . .
Poached salmon and an open bottle of wine in car,
he was driven to a beach of peppery-brown sand.
He came almost silently,
the ink in his veins compelling him
to explore and bear a story, if he lived to tell it.

The match, placed in his hand, soon flared
catching twigs and paper on fire,
warming the afternoon colours of Halloween.
There was no Cape Ann, rubber boots, or codfish
(improvisation being the sincerest form of fun).

As Nino bent forward I expected him
to leave a space between his hot Italian lips
and the cold, grotesque pink-lipped neck
of the decapitated Atlantic salmon,
but he didn't. He kissed the thing dead-on,
then drank the proffered glass of wine straight down
and recited "Long may your big jib draw" three times.
The rim of the glass was cleaned each time
with a quick splash of wine over the edge

as all toasted the screeching in of Nino Ricci.
With specks of rain crowning him, arms were linked,
and all gingerly tiptoed to the water's edge
where Nino dipped his hand,
maybe wondering if someone would push him
and he'd go falling into a deep wet expanse
with the last Newfoundland fish.

We left the beach,
leaving footprints in the hourglass-fine sand,
taking grains that would in time
leave Nino's shoes and, perhaps, his mind.

Dieter's Paradox
David Elliot

It's strange, but we lose
whenever we win
In our ongoing battle
to try to stay thin;

And, yet, stranger still,
if we so choose,
We can say that we win
whenever we lose!

Addiction
Trina J. Hiscock

But how can it be?
What wrong have I done?
I've only ever wanted what was best.
How was I to know?
I meant no harm, no hurt.
I wanted so much for myself,
For my loved ones.
Now I'm alone.
They want me no more.
Can I blame them?
I wouldn't want me either.
I say, believe in me;
They laugh.
I say, trust me;
They laugh.
Is there no easy way out?
Life can't possibly be this cruel.
I want to start over.
But how?
I feel ready to make it on my own.
What a fool they must think I am,
To say I need help like that.
What nerve!
I can help myself.
I have to forget my problems.
What's that?
A knock on my door?
"Come in!"
It's my friends.

What's that I see,
A joint?
"Come over to your old pal, be a friend.
Help me to forget."

Soft
(for Victoria)
Florence Antle

Soft as a flutter in the breeze
Soft as the sound of a chicken's sneeze
Soft as a snowflake on your nose
Soft as summer rain on your toes
Soft as the down on a baby chick
Soft as ice cream down to the last lick
Soft as a leaf when it falls to the ground
Soft as silence of not a sound.

Done
Iovana Pye

The darkness of night falls
And covers their minds;
Like a heavy blanket
It steals their thoughts.
But again soon they think;
Their thoughts begin to howl;
Their fears, their hopes,
Being invaded by dangerous souls,
Forcing within them
Mixed feelings of love and hate
For everyone—
Each night
The ritual
Is complete;
It is done.

Meetings
David Elliott

Monotone speakers,
Heat from the heaters.
Topics are boring;
People are snoring.

You Were Always There
Madelyn Corbett

Whether it was to listen,
whether it was to talk,

you were always there;

Whether it was to work,
whether it was to play,

you were always there;

Whenever I wanted your opinion
on something on my mind,

you made me feel special;

you were always there.

Wisdom
David Elliott

Wisdom comes with age, I'm told—
I should be glad as I grow old;
But if I could (I must confess),
I would stay young and know much less.

Teen Tales:

Discovering Limits

From My Classroom Window
Sarah Lynn Bussey

The big blue sky
The big spruce trees
The blowing snow
The cold strong breeze.

The whistling wind
The swaying trees
The sky-bound clouds
The cold strong breeze.

The snow-capped hills,
The frozen ice,
The low thick fog
Are all so nice.

Dreams
Amber Milley

It was a cold night in Vancouver. The autumn breeze blew across the blanket of leaves, picking them up and making them dance as the sun sank below the horizon. Somehow, I knew this would be the night I would never forget.

My name is Daizy Andrews or I *was* Daizy Andrews. Now I'm just a soul stuck between Heaven and Earth, waiting to be taken home where it all began . . . .

I was on my way home from work that evening when I spotted the old beggar woman.

She was dressed in black from head to toe. Long, wavy, gray hair framed her prune-like face. In her wrinkled hands she held a small black leather bag that seemed to hold death itself. It was not like me to invite strangers in—especially bums off the street—but the old lady looked so lonely and cold that I invited her to stay at my house for a night. She accepted gratefully. I don't know why I did it. It was as if something outside myself made me do it.

The old beggar walked into my house and sat on the floor of the guest room. My cat, Midnight, usually comes in and starts to rub against my legs and purr. She stopped dead in her tracks when she saw the old woman. Her black fur stood on end as she arched her back and hissed, her bright green eyes glaring at the old woman.

"Midnight," I asked, "what has gotten into you?"

The old beggar reached her long bony hand out to stroke my cat, but Midnight ran as fast as her little paws could carry her, out of the guest room, into the kitchen and under a chair.

A strange feeling came over me and I ran up to my room and locked the door. I was scared. It had something to do with the old woman's eyes.

I got into my blue pyjamas with the yellow polka dots and lay down on my bed. I tried to go to sleep. Instead, I tossed and turned. I always went to bed at twelve o'clock and fell asleep almost at once. Tonight was different. It was as if someone or something was stopping me.

Frustrated, I decided to go downstairs to get a glass of warm milk. Down the hall I went, past the guest room where the woman was staying, and into the kitchen. I placed my hand on the refrigerator door, opened it and peered inside the lighted box. I grabbed the milk carton. It was empty.

"Having trouble getting to sleep, my dear?" The old woman's question came from behind like a hook in my back. I must have jumped five feet.

"Yes," I gulped.

"Well, I have just the thing for that," she replied, reaching inside her black leather bag and pulling out a doll wearing pyjamas just like mine. The doll was as big as a large spoon and had long wavy red hair and a pale complexion like me.

"What do I do with the doll?" I asked curiously.

"Just put it under your pillow, and you will fall into a deep sleep," the woman said.

"Where did you get it?" I asked.

"You gave it to me, Daizy," the old woman replied as she ran out of the room.

The old lady is living on the streets, and she may be a bit crazy, but why does she know my name, and why does she say I gave her the doll? I didn't . . . or did I?

"Yeah, right! I never met you before!" I thought out loud. "And like a doll can really make me go to sleep!" With that I took the doll in my right hand and slam-dunked it into the trash can.

I ran back up the stairs to my room and climbed into bed, not realizing that the doll was now beside me. I fell asleep, entering a world filled with horror and anticipation. I was walking down the stairs searching for someone . . . or something. For what, I could not recall. It was dark in the house, and the walls were covered in red—like blood. I went through each room looking . . . . For what, I didn't know. I was approaching the guest room, reaching toward the cold metal knob, when the doorbell rang. I ran toward it feeling salty tears roll down my pale face. I opened the door to emptiness. I then ran back toward the guest room where the old lady slept. I opened the door in horror. There was my cat, Midnight, my only companion, split in two, with clumps of sticky blood on her matted black fur.

"What did you do to her?" I screamed at the old woman.

She was dressed in black and was dancing around the doll that at first had looked like me. Now, however, it looked different. It was stained in red, with a stick that looked like a little bone pierced through its stomach.

"The same thing I'm going to do with you!" the old woman yelled. Then she threw off her black cloak. What I saw was a gruesome sight. Underneath she had no skin. She was just a frame of rotting bones holding decaying organs which were infested with maggots. My stomach rolled in revulsion.

"You fell for it!" the skeleton exclaimed. "Didn't anyone ever tell you that you're not supposed to take anything from strangers?"

"I can't believe it!" I said. "I invited you into my house to sleep and you do this to me?"

She didn't say a single word. She just stood there as the silence swept over me. Then, without a word, she cracked her arm off and, whirling behind me, thrust it into my back! My intestines flew across the room in front of me and hit the wall with a gruesome splat!

I woke up in a cold sweat. Midnight! I needed to find her to see if she was okay. I ran down the stairs to the hall. My footsteps echoed through the silent, dark house. Then suddenly the sun came. It cast a red hue on the walls. I ran to every room looking for my cat. I was approaching the guest room as the doorbell rang. Deja vu swept over me as I remembered my dream. I grabbed my gun from the closet near the door. I didn't want to see the rotting skeleton dancing around the doll or my cat split in two. I pointed the pistol at my head, feeling compelled to pull the trigger . . . .

I woke up frightened and scared. I could not tell the difference between dreams and reality—if dreams fit into reality or if reality was a dream. I kept dreaming and waking to another dream. I pinched myself, thinking: maybe now I'm awake for good. But I was wrong. I glanced over beside me. There was the strange doll with its eyes closed.

As I started to cry, I heard the doorbell ring, then the chanting of the old beggar. My cry mingled with the sounds. Why is this happening to me? Why does this have to happen to me?

Now I am just a soul stuck somewhere in time between dreams and reality, waiting to be taken home where it all began.

A Wet Surprise
Marilyn Young

"Oh, that sun is hot today!" panted Jenny, sprinkling droplets over everything as she dropped down next to Molly on the blanket. "But that water sure is refreshing," she laughed as her friend, scowling at her, reached for a towel and dropped the book she was pretending to be engrossed in.   Half-heartedly, Molly grunted her acknowledgment.

"The river has gone down an awful lot these past couple of weeks," Jenny continued, undaunted, as she observed Molly surveying a group of boys horsing around near the dock.   Molly glanced over to the white pole marking the water level. Indeed the river had receded four inches. She turned to Jenny who was speaking again.

"You've been sitting here for an hour pouring over that novel. Are you planning on spending another summer just sitting on the beach, especially dressed like that in your jeans?" she asked.

"No, I am not!" Molly faced her friend, "but what can I do?"

"Well," Jenny replied, "you could take lessons if you wanted to learn how to swim so bad."

"But where?" Molly enquired. "We have no instructor at the public pool this year."   She stopped as a thought occurred. "Hey, what about you teaching me?"   Molly's heart plummeted to her stomach as her friend shook her head.

"I'm sorry, Molly, but I can't help you. I can manage to stay afloat but you know how you panic if you can't feel the ground under your feet. I just wouldn't be able to handle you. But . . . ."

"Why, Rick, of course!" Jenny exclaimed, ignoring the stricken look on Molly's face.

"You know how Rick loves playing and carrying on in the water. He wouldn't want to get stuck with a beginner like me." Molly hedged.

"Yeah," agreed Jenny. "The only way was if he really wanted to."

The girls settled back on their beach towels, each lost in their own thoughts. From the corner of her eye, Molly watched as Rick and his friends played on the dock nearby, jostling each other while their peals of laughter wretched each nerve.

Suddenly, Jenny jumped up. "I am going into the water again. Do you mind?"

Molly shook her head. "You go if you want. I'll stay here." She picked up her book, not noticing her friend shrug, and pretending not to watch as Jenny raced off toward the river. Instead of reading, Molly observed her friend as she splashed into the water. Soon Jenny was involved in a game of tag with Rick and his friends. Molly watched them as they splashed and ducked each other. It seemed like so much fun.

She glanced around behind her as she heard a girl squeal with delight. As Molly watched, a group of boys picked the girl up and carried her to the river bank. The next instant, she was thrown into the water. For the first time, Molly noticed that she was the only one left on the bank.   Then she saw Rick and his friends advancing toward her. Instinctively realizing their intention, Molly scrambled to her feet. But the boys were too fast. Hands caught her shoulders and ankles. She started to protest, but the boys were too absorbed in carrying her struggling form to pay much attention. The summer breeze whipped her long hair into her eyes as she sailed through the air. As she hit the water, Molly felt her breath squeezed from her.

Down, down she went. Flagging her arms and kicking her feet instinctively, she struggled to the surface. Trying to stay afloat, she reached her toes down to feel for the bottom of the river. Nothing! Realizing she was out over her head, Molly waved her arms as she tried to call out to Rick, who was standing on the bank watching her. Rick's answer was lost as she submerged under the water for the second time. Water filled her eyes and her ears, and replaced the air her lungs cried out for. Kicking desperately, Molly surfaced again. She saw Rick's stricken face as she sucked in fresh air and tried to fight off the blackness that was stealing over her eyes. Too tired to fight anymore, she felt the water enclose her again. Suddenly an arm snaked around her shoulders.

"Don't fight. Relax!" a voice commanded in her ear. Relief made her go limp. Before long, Rick had dragged her ashore.

Molly sat up coughing water and gasping for air. Anger consumed her. "Look, look what you've done!" she sputtered. "You've ruined my new jeans. I could . . .", she hesitated as, turning to her rescuer, she saw a look of deep concern on Rick's face.

Slowly, she realized he was speaking to her. "Gee, I am sorry, Molly. I didn't know you couldn't swim. Is that why we haven't seen you in the water so far this summer?"

Molly glanced quickly at Rick. Turning her head as tears welled up in her eyes, her anger forgotten, Molly nodded.

"Hey, you know what?" Rick almost shouted. "I could teach you how to swim. I'm a real good swimmer!"

Molly saw the excitement on Rick's face. "You mean you actually wouldn't mind?" she asked with trepidation, looking for confirmation.

"Heck no, it's the least I can do after we almost drowned you!" Rick exclaimed.

Molly started to laugh. Shakily, she rose to her feet, smiling, as Rick offered his hand in assistance.

"Well?" Rick asked, "when do you want to start?"

Molly smiled again. "Would you mind waiting until tomorrow? I think I have had enough of the water today." She turned to see Jenny coming toward them.

"Okay, see you tomorrow," Rick shouted, waving back at the girls as he raced to rejoin his friends.

"What was that all about?" Jenny asked as she took in Molly's wet appearance.

Molly grinned with pleasure. "It looks like I may learn how to swim this summer after all."

As Jenny accompanied her to make sure she got home all right, Molly couldn't help but enjoy the warm feeling she felt as she found herself looking forward to her upcoming swimming lessons.

Making a Mark
D. Jean Young

(This is an excerpt from <u>The Empty Room</u>, a novel-in-progress. Ted Dawson, a doctor's son, is a senior high school student seeing a psychologist because of a court-ordered treatment after he has been found guilty of assaulting his girlfriend. This is a record of one of his sessions, a time when he tells a story but avoids personal issues.)

"It's wet out there, today, Doc. Almost drowned on my way over." Ted took off his leather jacket and hung it on the coat rack in the corner. He pushed his hand through his short, wet hair, and rubbed the water off the back of his neck with the back of the sleeve of his Nike sweatshirt.

"Have a seat, Ted. And be glad my roof's not leaking anymore."

Ted stared up at the ceiling. Right above the chair where he usually sat, a metre-long stain spread out its tentacles. He gave Doctor Grayson an appreciative grin. "And I thought that was your version of the Rorschach ink blot test."

"Sorry. It's just a stain. Had to get the shingles fixed last week. Haven't gotten around to a paint job yet."

"Guess it'll have to come out of the payment for this week's chat with me."

"Guess so."

Ted took his last cigarette out of its package. In white letters on a black background the Surgeon General warned that "Cigarettes Cause Cancer." Ted laid his cigarette gently on the ashtray's edge. He removed the foil, rolled it into a compact ball between the palms of his hands. He tossed it into the ashes. It bounced and rolled to a stop. He lit his cigarette and inhaled deeply twice. He blew out smoke circles. Pale rings floated and dissolved as Ted began this day's story.

"Todd and me finished the pizza I bought, then he convinced me we were thirsty and needed to buy beer from our friendly neighbourhood bootlegger, the guy who sold beer and Similac to anyone who asked. We sat on the stairs by the closed-down movie theatre and planned how to start our gang.

"By the time we'd finished our dozen, we were rolling right along. The booze didn't seem to bother Todd that much. He *was* a bit more careful about where he put his feet as we walked on, toward my house. And his speech *was* a bit slower. But if you didn't know him well, you mightn't have noticed a thing. Because Todd was a good speaker, and he walked like a cat casually strolling across a peaked roof. Most people aren't even close to being as smooth as Todd was. Even after he'd had a half-dozen."

"Sounds like he impressed you."

"That's what I'm saying. I never asked him in when we came to my house. He said good-night and kept on walking down the road. As if he was going somewhere. I guess he was. But I still don't know where he lived. Maybe he was going to meet Mary Lynn—maybe he'd forgotten a date.

"We'd decided to start collecting members right away. Let a few in right from the start. Form a core group. Meathead and Mary Lynn had to be in. They stuck to Todd like stinging needle burrs in the fall. Besides, Meathead was strong, loyal, and a lot smarter than he looked. The

100

same went for Mary Lynn. Todd had a nose for quality.

"If I hadn't come along, he probably would have created a gang after a while without even trying. As they say in Chemistry class, I was just the catalyst.

"Catalysts make the flame happen. Get things going. Push all the dullness away. What do you think we did first, Doc?"

"Let's see. You wanted a uniform, deprivation, an ordeal, and a few mind-altering drugs. To start. Did I miss anything?"

"You're good, Doc."

"So. A uniform . . . . That should be the easiest, I'd say."

"You're right in a way. We picked a symbol. We made it an ordeal to get that symbol. Two for the price of one. And we skipped deprivation altogether." He stopped for a second. He stared blankly at the light switch. Gently, he rubbed a spot on the left side of his chest.

The doctor took a quick look at the ticking clock. "Go on."

"Well, that week, we chose three more to join with me, Todd, Meathead and Mary Lynn. We asked Meathead and Mary Lynn to help; ownership, feeling like you count—that's important. Meathead said, 'A-Anita Brooks. Sh-sh-sh . . . .'

" 'She,' I said.

"He nodded happily. 'She's good at planning things.' Sometimes Meathead gets stuck and if you say the first word for him, he gets on a roll and manages to get a whole sentence out at a time. Mary Lynn agreed. Todd, too. Anita's tall, heavy, dark-haired with a pasty kind of complexion and she wears glasses. Behind these glasses her brown eyes stare with a steely glint. She'd be no competition for Mary Lynn in the looks department, that's for sure.

"Mary Lynn picked Granger Robbins.

" 'He plays the guitar,' she said—'good for parties, and he's fast—best runner on the track team. Besides, he knows everything. Always got his ear to the ground.'

"A frown flashed across Todd's face when Mary Lynn mentioned Granger's name. But, as she talked, he listened, and he gave his okay. He knew he could hold his own with Mary Lynn. He wasn't going to let her think that he was worried about competition.

"'Karl.' Todd's choice was taller, bigger than Meathead and twice as mean. If we were into nicknames for the gang he would have been The Enforcer. But we never bothered with that. It was Mary Lynn's turn to cross her arms and draw her eyebrows together then. Karl had been her boyfriend before Todd. Word was he'd treated her rough—until she started carrying a knife. Karl respected guts. Mary Lynn patted her purse, where she still carried her knife. 'He'll do. No one's going to mess with us if we got Karl on our side.'"

"Sounds like an explosive mixture, Ted. Why would you want to be in the middle of all that?"

"Because of that. Because anything could happen. Because there was just enough wanting to be the best in this crowd to make them ready to do anything. There's nothing quite like living on the edge, don't you think, Doc?"

"If you say so, Ted. Do you need that?"

"Yeah. I do."

"Why?"

"It doesn't matter. You said I can tell you anything,

Doc, so let me go on with my story now."

"Whatever you say, Ted."

"My father was away for the weekend that we'd picked to make our start. That made things easier. Mom never asked me any questions. She'd just look at me with her worried look whenever I came in late.

"We met in an abandoned warehouse. Karl hauled the sleeve of his home-knit, grey wool sweater over his curled fist. He punched a hole in the window of the back door, reached in and opened the place up for us.

"Meathead was right about Anita. We'd all gotten together to plan the weekend, but she was the one who made sure everything was ready. She brought all the stuff we needed in a black garbage bag. Made of recycled plastic. 'Got to take care of our world,' she said. Waste drove her nuts. She even made us toss our Pepsi cans into those blue boxes.

"We pushed together a few old wooden crates to make a table. Anita covered it with a white linen tablecloth.

" 'Got it at Sally Ann's,' she said. On the tablecloth, she put out the bottles. Distilled water. Ink. Alcohol—not the drinking kind, the kind you use for disinfectant. Two forty-ouncers of Jack Daniels. Cans of ginger ale. Glasses—real ones; no non-degradable Styrofoam for Anita. Several small glass bowls and one big one made of steel. White towels. Stolen from a Howard Johnsons' laundry. Long, steel needles. Bandages. Paper towels. An electric kettle and a battery-powered plug-in. 'I've done some reading. And some listening,' she said. 'I know how it's done. I'm keeping it clean. But . . . it's going to hurt a bit at a time. I'm telling you now. If you can't stand pain, if you haven't got patience, now's the time to go. Is everyone in?'

" 'I am,' said Karl. Meathead just nodded. A little shiver shook Mary Lynn and she sucked her bottom lip, but she said, quietly, 'I'm in.' Granger's guitar was slung across his shoulder. He strummed it and sang, 'I will do that for love.' They all looked at me. 'Ready and waiting,' I answered, and we turned to Todd. 'I'll go first,' he said.

"Todd hauled off his plain white t-shirt and stretched out on the covered boxes. Anita had left a narrow section of about one metre by two clear. Sunshine crept in through the windows rimming the ceiling. Dust hung in the air. The warehouse felt big and silent. Hushed, even. No one said a word. Anita plugged in the electric kettle. Mary used a felt-tip pen to trace the design just to the right of Todd's left nipple. We'd agreed on that spot. A place where it wouldn't be seen unless you wanted it seen. A place that could be hidden if you wanted, revealed if you wanted that. We wanted an easy, simple mark. One with more than one meaning." Ted paused. He waited. Smiled at Doctor Grayson, inviting his question.

Doctor Grayson grinned back. He nodded "yes" and sighed as he shrugged his shoulders. "Okay. I'll bite. What was the design, Ted?"

"A swastika. A left swastika. For the terror of night. A sign that brings the sound of black boots and threatening armies to mind, right? But also a sign that means good fortune and prosperity."

"Anita's idea?"

"You got it, Doc. When she explained it, we knew it was perfect." Ted smiled again. "I like the way you make connections, Doc."

"Just doing my job, Ted."

"Sure. Let's go back to our warehouse now. Where Anita's sterilizing the long, steel needles in the steaming water. Where Granger's playing Queen's "Bohemian Rhapsody," sweet and low. Where Karl and Meathead are keeping watch. Mary Lynn kisses Todd's chest before she swabs it with alcohol. She's drawing on Todd's body."

"Where are you, Ted?"

"Watching, Doc. Taking it all in. Making sure I get the details in my memory."

"As if you're not really part of it all?"

"Oh, I'm part of it, Doc. More maybe than you realize. There's a way of getting people to do things, you know. Of picking up their scattered thoughts and putting them all together, making them real. Every play needs a director."

"But a director's not in the play."

"That's not important. Be quiet for a few minutes, Doc. I'm leaving soon; it's best to finish a story once it's started."

Ted's voice lowers as he moves into storytelling mode. The doctor leans forward slightly.

"Anita stretches Todd's skin. Dips one long, steel needle into the purple ink, pricks his skin. He winces. 'Don't do that,' she orders. 'Hold Mary Lynn's hand. Squeeze when you feel the needle touching. I got to go in deep enough to make sure the ink stains.'

"A bubble of blood surfaces. She blots it quickly with the recycled paper towel and continues along the line. She waits until the bubbles stop before she moves on to the next piercing. When at last she finishes one zigzag, she drops that needle into the steel bowl. 'Rest a bit now.' She washes her hands. 'I'll do . . . .' She looks around and settles on me. 'I'll start Ted next. We'll do the other side—the red side—after everyone has the purple done.'

"I wasn't about to take off my shirt, to show my back. So, I'd worn a button-up shirt. Cotton twill. I undid the buttons and took Todd's place on the bumpy crate. My back wasn't hurting. The Demon had been quiet for more than a month. This ritual came at a good time for me.

"And it had turned into a ritual. Mary Lynn kissed my chest, too—her lips soft on my skin. The alcohol swab was cold. The tracing of the felt tip sent spidery shivers along my body. Mary Lynn held my hand. The tiny stings of pain were easy for me. They didn't know how easy. I'd learned long ago how to push feeling away. And all while the needle stabbed, Granger played a sweet-sad melody I'd never heard before. He told me later that it was his own tune.

"Granger was next. Then Karl. Mary Lynn did Anita. Anita let Mary Lynn kiss her chest. But she refused to hold anyone's hand; I saw the white come into her knuckles as she balled her fist.

"Todd did the kiss, the swab and the drawing for Mary Lynn. She gripped Todd's hand and closed her eyes. A tear trickled along the side of her turned face when the needle first dug into her skin. But she didn't cry out or ask Anita to stop.

"Then the purple side was done. When we all held bandages to our upper chests, we drank Jack Daniels. Two half-glasses of whiskey each. Straight down. It burned when I swallowed.

"Anita refused her share. 'I want a steady hand,' she said. 'I'll make up my share on the end. Before Mary Lynn does me.'

"The ritual was repeated. It took a long time, but that didn't seem to matter. We'd planned to take the whole day. When we were finished, we went to a Chinese restaurant just down the street. I paid for our suppers. We went back to the warehouse, helped Anita pack up. We laughed and shouted, knowing each of us was hurting just a little and that we shared the pain. Knowing that we were different from anyone else in the town now. We were together in a special kind of way.

"We agreed on another ritual. A dangerous ritual. One that would weed out any weak links. Perhaps we shouldn't have pushed it to that limit. But, at the time, it seemed important to make a statement. To be dramatic. It was Todd's idea.

" 'Let's go on a journey—a pretend journey. But one we won't forget. Unless any of you are scared?' Such a challenge was a green light that day. He knew that. And I guess he wanted to make sure we knew he was the leader. Up to this point, he hadn't played a major part in this day.

'When I was little,' he said, 'I tripped across the railroad track one day. I was lucky. Because I fell flat on my back and the train rolled on over me. I wasn't hurt, and no one even knew it happened. Never told a soul. Not even my mother. She was alive then. Might have cut into my wandering ways if she had started to worry.'

" 'What's that got to do with us?' asked Karl.

" I had a feeling I knew. My heart beat hard at the thought. Todd went on. 'To finish our initiation, let's try that trick again. There's an eight-fifteen train. Only a short one. Twenty cars. I've counted. I say we stretch out, all seven of us along the track. Let the train roll over us. We'll have to be still and once the train is coming, there's no chickening out. Unless you want to be ready for the

Colonel.'

" 'I don't want to do that,' said Mary Lynn. 'It's stupid.'

" 'So, you're scared already,' sneered Anita. 'I'll bet you'll sit out anything that might get a bit too hairy. Maybe I should scrape off that tattoo right now.'

"Karl laughed. 'Yeah, Mary Lynn. Maybe we should all help her.'

" 'Okay, okay. I'll do it. But I don't have to like it.' Mary Lynn wasn't about to let Karl see her as being weak. If the girls were ready to lie down under the trains, well, then, what could the rest of us do?"

"You could have backed up Mary Lynn."

"No, Doc. That wasn't an option. Not on that day. You had to be there." Ted went on with the story. "It was dark by eight o'clock. We picked out our stations. Far enough away from the crossroads not to be noticed. Spread out like dashes over a space of about fifteen metres or so. We tied our laces securely. Buttoned our buttons so there was nothing loose. Anita, Mary Lynn and Granger tied back their long hair so no stray strands would catch.

" 'When the time comes, lie flat. Real flat. Lie still. Try not to think,' Todd ordered.

"I took up the position closest to the oncoming train. Then there was Karl, Anita, Granger, Mary Lynn, Meathead, and, finally, Todd.

"Todd had put his ear to the rail. 'It's coming. Listen! Hear it?'

"We all knelt to hear. We heard the vibration of the train humming through the metal. One by one, we settled down flat and straight along the middle of the track. Crazy thing to do. Hard to believe we considered such a thing now.

"But on that night, we felt as if we could do anything and survive. So we lay there, stretched out, and I remember the thundering roaring sound that made me want to run, screaming, and it was coming down toward me, and the smell of grease and creosote soaked into me, and then the blackness and the grinding as the train was coming down, going on and on forever, forever, forever rolling, screeching and thundering over me. Once it started, I couldn't have moved. Not even if I had wanted to. I was pinned to the ground. But still, even then, I couldn't scream. Because, even if I screamed, the train would still keep on coming.

"After a few hour-long minutes, when I had been numbed and was trembling, there was a rush of cool, fresh air and I could breathe again and the train was past me. I sat up, trembling; one after the other—Karl, Anita, Granger, Mary Lynn, and Meathead—arose. Like figures rising from graves.

"We all looked at the train, charging down the tracks. And we all saw that Todd was being dragged We ran after the train, stumbling on the tracks. Mary Lynn fell. I helped her up. Todd fell off about thirty metres down the track. When we reached him, his eyes were open. But we knew he couldn't see. He must have moved when the train rolled on by; he'd got caught up in a gear or something, I suppose. He got thumped along until his brain was bumped into mush. Mary Lynn started crying.

" Anita said, 'I hope he signed an organ donor card.'"

Prejudice
Natasha Strickland

An innocent girl
From a different race
Has hurt feelings,
A darker-coloured face.

A boy, in hatred,
Not knowing why,
Has spoken things
To make her cry.

She is just different—
Why do they fight?
Hatred has brought darkness
And blocks their light.

Fantastic Imaginings:

Making Possible the Impossible

Khalen of Klyn
Vaughn Harbin

Where now the wasted Barrens lie
Beneath fair Terra Nova's sky,
Once there stood the kingdom of Klyn,
In every world, a world within.
All was quiet in the evening air,
And the silence seemed tangible everywhere,
When out of the darkening forest glade,
Rode the horseman of Klyn with his fearsome blade
Held high in a hand adrip with blood,
Came Khalen of Klyn with thundering thud
Of iron-hoofed horse aspattering the mud,
Came Khalen of Klyn adrip with blood.
The silver orbed moon shone in dim disarray
As the vanishing horseman sped away,
Over the foothills, across the plain,
To the outskirts of the Elvan domain,
Then on through the shimmering, silver shade,
On to the Elvan King's stockade,
Like the cresting wave of a river in flood,
Came Khalen of Klyn adrip with blood.
The heart of the Elvan king turned cold
At the sound of the message Prince Khalen told,
When with sword held high and thundering thud,
Came Khalen of Klyn adrip with blood.
Quoth the king in royal anger, rude,
"It is enough! This viper's brood
That stalks the Elvan Forest's shade
Shall lately taste keen Elvan blade!
But, softly now, my princely one,

What hast the Wasting Wanton done?
How now thy royal figure slips,
The rosy colour flees thy lips!
To the prince, fair courtiers, one and all!
There, spread thine arms to break his fall.
Thus, steady his arm, his foot, his hip,
Khalen of Klyn is with blood adrip!"
"Nay, nay, oh King of the Magic Wood,
My wounds but bleed as pure hearts should
whene'er is heard the Wanton's wail
Within the green and peaceful vale.
Grieve not for princely knighthood's pain,
For wounds as these I count as gain!
Each suffered not its pulsing flow
Until it, too, had dealt a blow."
And so they helped him to his steed,
And so he led them with all speed,
Till they came within the Wanton's rage,
Prince, and pauper, and King, and page;
For, the Wasting Wanton—the Devil's churl,
Sought the soul of each boy and girl,
And had vowed to keep them forever bound,
In a place ever lost, in a land never found.
They fought him bravely, they fought him strong.
They battled the Wasting Wanton long,
Till there stood but a man 'twixt Heav'n and Hell,
And then the valiant Khalen fell,
But not before his royal blade
A fearsome mortal wound had made
Deep in the heart of the Wanton's breast.
Fair Khalen of Klyn, forever blest!
Scarce yet a day had passed its shade

Since the horseman of Klyn with his fearsome blade,
Held high in a hand adrip with blood,
Had ridden the forest spattering the mud.
But, oh, for the kingdom of king bereft!
Oh, for the pitiful remnant left!
And, ah, for the women of Klyn who sought
Their sons alive, and found them not.
Like sparrows and wrens in the evening sky,
That to their nestings, homeward fly,
So had their gallant spirits flown,
By pure, angelic zephyrs blown.

Upon the moor, a lone heart kneels
'Mid Heaven's sparks and thunder peals.
'Tis Aleah of Klyn, the Northern Rose,
Upon whose face the North Wind blows.
Could writer tell, could artist show,
Such drama, framed against the glow
Of muted mauve voluminous cloud,
As fair Aleah's figure, bowed.
Her noble face o'er his so pale,
Her billowing cape in the gathering gale,
Her words of love, his fading breath,
Lips red with life, lips pale with death!
With the auburn silk of her tresses, fair,
With feminine glory, with her own hair,
She wiped the tears of pain that told,
Alone, how suffered the knight, so bold.
And as his eyelids struggled to ope',
Her heartbeat rose in rhythmic hope,
And willed warm life into his form,
Her breast a fury, her love a storm!

"Foul Hell beneath! Fair Heaven above!
Touch not the soul of the man I love!"
She cried, with hands stretched in the air,
Wild flames of passion in her auburn hair.

All is silent, now, in the breaking dawn,
And all these figures long since gone.
Where, now, the wasted Barrens lie
Beneath fair Terra Nova's sky,
A beauteous voice calls from the sea.
Fair Aleah? Brave Khalen? Who calls to me?
Here, once, there stood the kingdom of Klyn,
In every world, a world within.
And over the mist-shrouded, mournful moor,
Is heard the wind, wailing evermore
For a world in every world within,
And Aleah, pleading for Khalen of Klyn . . .

. . . 'Tis Aleah, pleading
        For Khalen of Klyn . . .

. . . Aleah is pleading . . .
        For Khalen of Klyn.

Letter from 1992
Nellie P. Strowbridge

The year was 2117—two hundred and fifty years since Canada was born, and, for the sake of tradition, the Canadian government intended to honour the past. A time capsule that twelve people from ten provinces and two territories had sealed in Ottawa in 1992 was to be opened as part of the official ceremonies.

Janalee Kennedy had heard about it, but she didn't give it much attention until the buzzer in her thumb ring alerted her to a crisp message on her computer. She had been chosen to go to Ottawa and open a letter that had been written on paper by one of her forebears in 1992 entitled "Address The Future."

No one used paper any more. Janalee knew that generations ago trees were cut down for that purpose. For a long time it was the only means of recording what was happening. But this had to be a joke or—a virus in her computer!

The message was real. It's strange, mused Janalee, how a 125-year-old letter can stop a person in her tracks and turn her back to a lifetime that was before hers.

Until this moment, time seemed to be moving so fast, it was as if days closed up behind her, obliterating her thoughts of events and people—except for a piece of herself she considered missing. A childhood trauma had given Janalee her motivation to train as a genetics specialist. She wondered what her sister, Nancy, would have looked like had she been allowed to be born. When doctors discovered that she carried chromosomes found to contain the manic depressive gene she was given a name and then aborted. Long before Janalee's generation, specialists had isolated myriad genetic weaknesses that resulted in a host of diseases. But not until her generation, and only after she was born, was there mandatory testing for all pregnancies. Janalee was fortunate to be alive. No matter what defects she carried inside herself she was safe—so far.

With a health care system heavily burdened, due to Canada's many medical crises and the longevity of its population, Government had, a decade ago, decided that it was ethically liable for making sure children were born physically and mentally fit. Women and men wanting to have babies now had to have their genes screened, and if any actual or potential defect or disease was found in their chromosomal structure, they would not be licensed to become parents. It wasn't a perfect solution. Testing wasn't 100 per cent accurate, and sometimes children were born with—or later developed—defects or diseases. Janalee shuddered at the thought that eventually all newborn children would have to pass a test in order to remain alive.

Scientists were working to perfect a laboratory womb where gene designers would go through donors' DNA chains, destroying defective genes and replacing them with genes free of defects. Offspring created between a man and a woman could become a thing of the past. Janalee let out a sigh whenever she thought of that possibility. She wanted to have the experience of creating life from within her own body so she could carry on living separate from herself. Children might even become obsolete if scientists were successful in their efforts to isolate the aging gene and delete its time bomb. If healthy people could be kept alive, there could be a moratorium placed on human reproduction.

Janalee's father, Clarence, and her brother, Michael, who were both into environmental studies, contended that isolating the aging gene in humans wouldn't be of much value unless people were willing to save the earth from human-inflicted pollution. And there were always new diseases to threaten human survival. Acquired Immune Deficiency Syndrome had destroyed one-third of the world's population before a cure was found. Janalee had learned in her history studies about two heroes of their time: Christopher Upshall and Mary Peddle shared a Nobel Peace Prize after introducing into human cells a molecule from a cockroach. It regenerated the immune system and people suffering from AIDS recovered. Still, no one could be sure that the human immune system would ever be free of endogenous or external attacks.

"Sometimes, I wonder," Janalee murmured within earshot of her mother, "how far scientists will go into human exploration—and exploitation of genes."

Lillian, who didn't like to think about such things, warned: "Thinking too much can cause brain erosion. "You should," she admonished, "live to do your day's work and that's no bad shame. Anything else is someone else's job. Your father's great-grandmother Liz Emma Kennedy passed down that advice."

Her mother would probably look like her grandmother if she hadn't had plastic surgery, and she'd be just as short if she hadn't had a spinal graft to make her taller. No one knew any more who anyone's offspring resembled because as soon as people got old enough to go for beauty consultation, they changed the part of themselves that resembled their relatives. Some people had so many surgical beauty enhancements they no longer looked like themselves.

Janalee pressed a button on her wall-to-ceiling communication centre to summon her university professor on the screen. Mr. Clayton was eccentric by his own admission, and had chosen to remain bald as a sign of virility. He began his lecture in high gear. His cobalt blue eyes widened, then were squeezed tight as if by a brain that had no other way to execute a sentence: "Humans," he bellowed, "are affected by faulty chromosomes to begin with, and through the centuries their genetic being has been eroded by environmental elements." He continued, his heavy eyebrows lifting above the caves of his 'now you see them, now you don't' eyes, "Maybe the original human was perfect. We have begun to make humans perfect again. Leaving the work up to nature proved to be hazardous. Look what she turns out!"

"Us!" Janalee answered, after pressing a button on her monitor so the professor in his studio could see and hear her.

"It didn't do a half-bad job on you," the professor laughed. Janalee pressed a button on her wrist bracelet and one wall became a solid mirror. She studied her face. It was small and round—and, she had to admit, ordinary. She didn't know why other people thought she was beautiful. Her mouth was large around evenly spaced teeth. A slight gap between her two front teeth had been fixed years ago. Her shoulder-length hair was cinnamon brown, a match for the few powdery freckles sprinkled on the bridge of her nose. Her blue eyes looked back at her enigmatically. What strange sights would they pitch on, she wondered.

Janalee switched off the mirror, and turned back to the professor who was saying that "identifying the genes that control each physical structure and mental characteristic has resulted in healthier longer-living humans. In fact, doing away with just two parents will allow communal genetics. Fertilized eggs from several women will be fused and foreign microorganisms injected into them— perhaps a bacterium and a virus—to give the resulting new life immunity to diseases that may attack it. Offspring will have no genetic identification to parents. The state will raise children with a communal responsibility."

The professor leaned back and smiled as if he'd just discovered Utopia. Janalee pressed a button and the professor disappeared. She did not want her genes passed on without any filial identity. It wasn't normal for men and women not to be allowed to retain the exclusive use of their own genes in producing offspring. She felt an urge to escape. There must be some place she could go and live naturally, a place where the world wasn't artificially inseminated with technology.

She lay back on her massaging mattress, letting it relieve her tense muscles, imagining the feel of the paper letter under her fingers. She pressed the soundproof switch on the wall and shut out the sounds outside her room. She needed time to think about 1992. It was such a long time ago. What was it like back then? She had never thought much about the past. Her mother said her namesake, Janalee Amelia, was back there. Information had been passed down, but much of it had been lost in the fire that killed her grandmother Sara Ann Taylor. Before she went blind, the tall, stately woman with wisps of fine hair around her forehead used to read to Janalee from a book called Widdershins—meaning "turning back the clock."

Janalee had seen, but had never held in her hands, some old books kept under glass in the town's archival library. She had never thought about it until now, but it was odd that her grandmother had to turn the pages to read. Janalee suddenly felt fortunate that she had a compu-reader. Words slid away as she read on it, her finger slightly touching an arrow key.

A memory flittered against her thoughts for a brief moment, then was lost. She tried to pull the memory back, and then it came so strong it was as if she was back to when she was a little girl looking into her parents' bedroom drawer and seeing a rectangular object made of paper. Her mother said it was an envelope containing a letter that wasn't to be opened. She later found her mother crying because the letter had been destroyed.

Hor mother's brother, Reuben, who suffered from a drinking disease, had come to their home looking for funds. He knew his sister had won one of the last lotteries the government allowed before it decided that no one should get rich by exploiting poor people. They often gambled a little and lost a lot.

Reuben hadn't been given a share of his sister's money for fear he would use it unwisely. He had pushed his sister aside and found the envelope. Muttering that he knew it was stuffed with old bank vouchers, he had ripped it open. When he saw that it contained only a letter—and an outdated one at that—he tore it to shreds and fed it to the garbage disposal. Janalee wondered now if it could have been a copy of the archived letter.

On her way into the Parliament buildings in Ottawa, Janalee felt a sense of timelessness, as if she and those who had gone before her had spanned generations to become one. She knew that every person lives inside a memory, and that part of it can be carried by the lives of those who come after. Those who are gone can continue to exist inside that memory.

As she held amber-coloured sheets of textured parchment tied with gold- and black-trimmed ribbons, Janalee saw the delicate silver charm of faith, hope and charity, symbols of the Christian strength she carried inside herself.

She began to read the letter from 1992—the tangible evidence of her forebear's life—in front of Prime Minister Elizabeth Maley, distinguished guests and the eleven other descendants. As she read, Janalee felt as if her forebear's memory was in her voice, emitting the strength of the woman who had written the words with a conviction that spoke of faith in country and people. The voice of the woman whose body once held part of her genetic code compelled her to turn around and go toward the past.

Inside the envelope, Janalee's fingers touched a silver chain holding a delicate, tiny seashell. Its lacy-shaped openings must have been crocheted by the sea over a millennium. The 2117 committee advised her that it could locate the beach where the seashell had been found and project a picture to her with all its sights and sounds. But Janalee wanted to go to the beach where her forebear had been.

Once she had directions, Janalee pressed the buttons on her car-plane's compu-disk to feed in necessary information. She didn't mind travelling alone; solo air travel was relatively safe now that there were sensors and repellents to other vehicles.

A lone, white cloud hung in the azure sky as her little car-plane touched down on Kennedy beach in Hibbs Cove. She pressed a lever and her door slid open to a place where there were no tele-noises. She stepped down onto a tiny beach in a cove that looked as if it had always been unpeopled. She stood watching water lap at her feet, then slip back to be enveloped by the ocean. Pulpy knobbed sea kelp swayed playfully against barnacled rocks.

Janalee began to walk across the coarse sand and talus stones, and it was as if she were walking in other people's footprints. She pulled a sprig from a boy's love bush rising from a rock in the sand, and a bluebell from a cranny in the side of jagged, grey cliffs. They reminded her of the pressed shrub and flowers in her grandmother Taylor's Bible.

She could hear whispers, even laughter in the wind. Ghostly fingers touched her face in gentle strokes. She watched gulls: satin white and saddleback, circling and pitching on 150-foot cliffs.

Scientists contend that everything said and every scene once created, always exists, waiting for powerful stimulus to develop it. Suddenly it was as if the life that had been in those people who lived and worked in this cove surfaced. From her subconsciousness there emerged a genetic memory that must have been first stored in her forebears' bodies.

She saw square and rectangled yellow and white houses built on hills and cliffs; beside them were blood-brown fish stores, some leaning toward the sea. Across the cove she saw a wharf and boats tied to it, and against the cliffs, weather-darkened stages where fish were bulked. Stage heads sat in front of them, their laps holding tables for splitting and gutting fish, and puncheons for washing them in. There were men in oilskins slitting bellies of fish, and women in brightly coloured, oil-painted barbels gutting them as fast as a blink. The straight legs of the stages stood angled, and partly hidden in the salt water of the cove, some holding a footing jammed in the rugged rocks jutting up from the sea bed. The sea, a liquid mass of living substance, folded under, then rolled over itself, its milky green waters fringed with lace that changed patterns, then fell apart. White floating spots rocked gently in the water.

As a skiff put-putted into the cove, Janalee heard women calling into the wind : "Jake and the crew must have lots of fish; the gunnels are low."

There was a life about the cove that was not just of the sea and place—but a life of a people who lived with the taste of the salt of the ocean on their lips and the breath of the wind in their lungs, and the love of life in their veins.

Janalee looked up a steep path and saw the image of a woman helping another woman carry a handbarrow full of fish, ivory-coloured by the sun, and flattened into a maple leaf shape. She was a tall woman with strong-looking legs under her barbel apron. She heard someone call, "Aunt Liz Emma."

The images of the cove people left as suddenly as they had come and once again the cove looked as if there had never been anyone living there.

Suddenly Janalee saw a scattering of seashells among tiny stones and coloured opaque glass lying close to the grey cliffs away from the sea. She picked up a seashell, holding her breath, as she slipped the seashell off the chain around her neck and laid the two sides together. They connected in perfect symmetry.

As she started to leave the beach, Janalee looked back and saw her footprints in the sand. Dusty green water rolled in over them and they were no longer footprints, just some markings. They too would disappear. But she would leave her mark. She would find a way for children to be born naturally. She had to. Otherwise, family trees and the continuity of their seed would be no more.

Abstract Vision
Janalee A. Strowbridge

I am one
with the sea,
wind and sky;
all that is real,
all that is here completes me;
I am whole
and it is mine.
The fragrance of mist
is sprayed over my body,
my spirit is revived
by the call of the
creatures that engage
below my aqueous ground.
The earth brings forth

vast visions of what
my eyes cannot hold.
This life that I embody
captures all forms of breath,
through its rainbow of beauty;
life that can exhale satisfaction,
if you inhale it.
Radiance is cast over the earth
it is cast over me.
I feel the warmth,
I know what is true,
what is real.
It is a journey one can only
feel to understand.
To experience the power of the earth,
its dirt and breath
and all that can be visually inhaled
surrounds us every day
and its reflections of life to be
are captured in the water, the wind and the sky.

The Final Wish
Sarah Penney-Flynn

He will be waiting—a vision in the darkness of the rain that chills her skin.

Icy fingers draw the warmth from the blood that runs in her veins. The thoughts that haunt her mind are beyond her grasp, beyond limits of what she has become. She retreats into the folds of her canvas raincoat, her hesitant footsteps tattooing an uneven rhythm on the wet pavement. She is uncertain as she nears the bridge, unsure of the memories that overtake her soul as she recognizes the sweet murmur of the waves against the pilings. The faint, clear scent of the river fills her nostrils. She had almost forgotten.

"Andrew?" Her voice drowns in the silence as she reaches out to lean against the bridge railing, the damp steel unfamiliar against her palm. "Andrew, it's me."

The night brushes against her like a stray black cat. For a moment she wishes that she hadn't come. There is too much of the past here. And then he emerges from the shadows, and she restrains the urge to turn and run back into Forever. Even through the shroud of rain and mist, she can feel the endless depth of his brown eyes absorb her fear, her uncertainty. The memory of him swells in her, and she realizes that she had forgotten the power he holds over her, his love like a web from which she cannot escape.

"Claire?" He whispers her name, as the ghost of a smile lingers over his mouth. He wears the expression of one who is wearied of fighting and who has allowed the Fates to cast him into the emptiness below despair. "I . . .

I thought that maybe it was my imagination."

"No, it isn't." She does not let herself reach out to touch him although the desire to hold him is like a fiery brand in her soul. "Don't you think I'm real?" she asks. "You knew that I wouldn't leave, not truly."

His face is shadowed by the dim sliver of light from a street lamp that cuts through the black rain. Her breath is swept away by the beauty of his smile, and his eyes cast against the ebony darkness like a sculptor's image. Like an angel, she finds herself thinking, and she almost laughs at the irony.

His voice falters, and he smiles sadly. "Sometimes I think that you never were real." He reaches out tenderly, hesitantly, to brush his hand against her cheek as if to assure himself that she is not an apparition. The familiar gesture scares her. It is all a part of her past, fragments of who she is . . . was. It confuses her, this merging of two worlds. "You are so beautiful."

She is wearing the dress that she wore the first night she met him, the fabric soft and smooth against her skin, a pale creamy yellow that accentuates her shallow complexion and dark brown eyes. She can remember the way he looked that night, down by the shore, laughing across the slithering flames of the fire amidst a group of her friends. She had sat and watched him, shivering, and then he had been there beside her, bending over to introduce himself. He had captured her heart that one night. "Andrew, you know that I haven't come here to talk about . . . then." She stands motionless, as if she is part of the night itself.

"I know," he responds, lowering his eyes, ruffling his cropped honey hair nervously. She closes her eyes against the musky scent of his cologne. "I . . . I didn't know what to do when you left . . . were gone . . . I had no one to turn to; it was like you'd never been there. I kept wondering if you had been in pain. What if I had picked you up from work that day?"

"Shush!" She grasps his trembling shoulder, trying to absorb the memory, to make him forget, even though she knows that no one ever forgets.

"Everyone was so kind at the funeral." A single tear stains his cheek. "I hated them for being so kind. I wanted them to hate me, like I did. Your mother—she cancelled everything: the flowers, the cake, the caterers . . . . She came to take your dress." He is crying now, unashamed. "I couldn't, Claire. I couldn't let her take it. It smelled like you."

She pulls him to her, cradling his head on her shoulder. His tears are burning her skin, his body warm and helpless in her arms. "Everyone was so glad that they caught the guy who . . . killed . . . you, but he got out a year later. I sat home every night, wanting to kill him." He is clinging to her, as if she can keep him from crossing the boundaries of darkness.

"Shush!" She is astonished by the pain she feels, an unending ache that passes through her body. She wants to grasp it, to make it real, but it is beyond her reach. "I know." She hesitates, limp, as the reflections from that evening overwhelm her. "The restaurant had been busy. I wasn't paying attention when I left. The road was empty. He appeared out of nowhere. It hurt for a few minutes. All I could think about was you." She reaches up to caress his cheek. "I could have sworn you were there, holding me. I could hear the sirens, the paramedics. And then, when I heard your voice and I knew I couldn't come to you, I let go."

She can feel his limbs tense under his jacket before he steps away. His face is masked by bitter revulsion. "You left? Just like that, Claire. Do you know what you left me with?"

"Don't you think I cried when I saw your tears?" She is pleading. She won't ever forget those nights when she sat in the dimness of his bedroom, yearning to wipe away his emptiness, to hold him, yet all she could do was watch. "I cried, too, because a love like ours can't ever be erased by the distance between heaven and earth. Andrew, I was standing there, by your side at the funeral. I was there when you failed your medical exam. I was there," the words strangle her, "when you came to this bridge to throw yourself into the river. I was there when you were offered the job at the clinic, too." She leans over to brush his shoulder. "Andrew, I was there when you met Jennifer." She tries to overcome the helplessness that rises in her at the name of the young medical student whom Andrew had met at the clinic. She had stood there, next to him, and had felt his appreciation for this concerned being who seemed to understand his pain. Then she had realized that this was the way it was supposed to be.

His legs collapse and he slumps toward the ground, supported only by the thick steel rails. He buries his head in his hands. "Claire, I . . . ."

She crouches next to him, shivering at the raindrops that chill her spine. "I don't know why I was allowed to come back, but I was, Andrew. Jennifer loves you with all of her heart and soul." Claire's tears mingle with the rain. "I am gone. Gone. You have to understand and accept that. I've seen it, Andrew—the way our life would have been if only that driver had been sober. I've seen our wedding . . . our children. It's beautiful, but it's not what happened. I will love you always. So does Jennifer; there's a part of me in her. There's a part of me in you. You have to let go. You have to."

"I don't want to let go!" He raises his voice over the murmured anger of the river. "I love you, Claire. I need you. I need that life that would have been ours."

She smiles sadly as he lifts his eyes to hers, the eyes that possess her mind, soul, and spirit. She has been warned against revealing what she has seen beyond this world—warned of the consuming darkness in between, but in his eyes she drowns. She raises her flushed cheeks to the stinging shards of rain and whispers the prayer, the calling . . . .

The dim moonlight sifts through the net curtains that hang limply from the nursery window, sprinkling mottled freckles of liquid gold across the smooth cheek of the sleeping form. Claire bends over the crib, brushing her lips along an exposed pug nose. The child moves, restless under the cocoon of quilts, lost in deep slumber.

"Claire?" Andrew is there, at the door, framed against the light that spills in from the corridor, his briefcase dangling against his legs. "Is Emily asleep?"

"Yes." She is astounded still by his handsome form. Even in a rumpled suit with his tie carelessly undone, with his hair dishevelled, he possesses an innocence, a strength. Grey hairs have begun to blend with his honeyed curls, yet his eyes hold as many secrets as in youth. He still takes her breath away. "She just fell asleep—but not before I read *Little Miss Chick* three times."

He laughs softly, the sound wrapping itself around her spirit. "Did you do the voices?" He rests his briefcase against the door frame and comes to her.

"Yes, sir." She teases him playfully, slipping her arms around his waist. "So, how was your day?"

He leans over and kisses Emily softly. Claire can see the pride in his eyes as his face is caught in the evening light. She feels an odd urge to hold him to her, to never let him go. "Actually, my day was bearable," he answers. "We had an important meeting with the hospital board to discuss the possibility of a new cardiovascular wing. I missed you." He envelops her in his arms greedily. "Let's have a nice leisurely supper, then maybe watch a movie."

"I'll tell you what." She rests her head against his shoulder in the familiar scent of his jacket, then adds, "I've got spaghetti casserole in the oven, and with the help of a sweet romantic husband I might be able to arrange a magical evening." She smiles happily.

They are interrupted by a tiny gurgle, and Claire turns to ease Emily into her arms. "What's wrong, baby?" She strokes the porcelain-like cheek fondly. "Andrew, why don't you go on downstairs. I'll put little Miss Princess back to sleep; then I'll be down."

"Okay." He lingers to look at them silhouetted against a golden veil of the sun's setting light. She longs to make him stay here with them, but she must let him go.

He leans forward to press his lips on hers, and she allows herself for one moment to surrender to the past, the present and the could-have-been . . . .

She awakes from her dreaming to his urgent touch, as cold mud clings to her bare skin. She turns her head from the rain's piercing stab, her spirit limp and drained.

"Come on, Claire." She can hear his voice, distant through the haze that fills the hollows of her body. "Come on. Where are you?" He brushes the hair away from her forehead, gathering her into his arms. "I love you."

"Andrew!" The word tickles her lips as it drifts from the very depths of her existence. She clings to him, forcing past the darkness that threatens to enclose her. "I . . . ." She catches her breath as he eases her to her feet, holding her against him protectively.

She knows that it is time. She has given of herself, but now she is helpless. He must find his own strength.

"I . . . ." His breath is hot on her cheek. "We had . . . we were going to have a baby. Is she . . . ?"

"She is with me," Claire says weakly. "We wait for you every day. She sends you her love. She's precious, Andrew." Claire lifts her fingers to his lips. "She looks just like you."

He lowers his eyes from her gaze. "You can't stay."

"No." The ache is felt in the recesses of her being. The ache for happiness, for hope, for him. "I'll never forget, Andrew. Jennifer loves you. There's a little boy waiting for the two of you. He's got your eyes and her smile. He needs his father."

She is weak now. She is called, and she has no choice but to go. "You have to go on, Andrew—for yourself and for me." She can feel herself fading in his arms; she can feel his grip tighten. She strains to bring her lips to his ear. "I am the wind that caresses you and the moonlight that touches your lips." The warmth of his lips on hers is the last sensation she feels as she merges with the wind, the blackness, the rain.

Andrew stands silently for a moment, tall and

unbending, as he touches the pale yellow scarf that he holds loosely in his hand. Then he turns toward the distant city lights and lets the scarf fall from his grasp into the water below.

The Ghost of Sawroad Hill
Jean Legge Hiscock

Old Abe had lived for sixty years
And never asked for much,
Just to stand behind his sawmill
And to guide it with his touch.

Each brand new piece of lumber,
Sweet-smelling on his land,
Meant so much more than all the work
Of any sculptor's hand.

But then one absent-minded moment
When he'd paused to rub his jaw,
His other hand upon a log
Had lurched against the saw.

There was no pain, just lots of blood
Splashing against the door,
Old Abe could not believe his eyes:
His hand lay on the floor!

They found him there next morning
A stiff and bloodied man;

They took him from his lumbermill,
But they never took his hand.

There is some talk, now I am told,
Of a ghost on Sawroad Hill;
It works away at the lumber pile
At Abe's old lumbermill.

And late at night, when the moon is high,
If you walk across his land,
You will never see old Abe himself—
You will only see his hand.

Men and Women:

Loving and Leaving

The Human Guinea Pig
David Elliott

When I promised to help my wife, Diane, with her plans to become a Registered Nurse, I didn't realize that my commitment would be the same as donating my body to medical science research.

"Dave, come and see what I brought home!" she called out excitedly, a few days after she had started the program.

It was during the time of year when we kept our wood stove burning, and it was with great effort that I forced myself from my favourite chair which is located next to the stove. With my body temperature somewhere between broil and BBQ, I shuffled to the room which we had set up for a study area. There she stood, smiling happily, and proudly holding a stethoscope.

"Let me practise on you!" she said, her enthusiasm equal to that of a five year old on Christmas morning.

"OK," I agreed, taking off my shirt.

Becoming conscious of my fleshly overhang as I looked in the mirror, I did what most men do in such situations to try and convince themselves that their physiques are not as bad as they look: I sucked in my gut. This move made me feel a little better because it exposed the belt buckle which my wife had given me on my forty-fifth birthday. The buckle said "Hang Over."

In the meantime, while I was concentrating on me, the future nurse had moved in and planked the metal stethoscope squarely on my chest. Under normal circumstances this would have caused no problem; however, the circumstances were not normal. The instrument was icy cold, and when its frigid face came into contact with my hot flesh, a series of events took place. My chest muscles went into a spasm; my abdomen slumped; the belt buckle disappeared. I pulled back from the shock, made a deep inward gasp, and sucked in a piece of lint that just happened to be floating in front of my face. In a sudden fit of coughing, I wheeled around and banged my left elbow on the corner of the study desk. Then the cat, whose tail I had stepped on in my frantic attempt to survive, attacked me and left a six-inch gash on the calf of my right leg and two tooth prints on the big toe of my left foot.

The next evening I sat again in my special chair, carefully tending a calf muscle that was bandaged in six yards of gauze wrap, and nursing a swollen elbow that had to be kept in a sling. As the heat from the stove helped me approach a state of total relaxation and comfort, I heard a voice from the distance filtering into my world of near bliss. "Dave, come and see what I brought home!" it said excitedly, bringing me back to reality.

In a semi-hypnotic trance, I grunted to my feet and limped to the room. There stood my wife, smiling happily and proudly displaying a blood pressure cuff.

"Let me practise on you!" she said with the same innocent enthusiasm she had exhibited the evening before.

"Not after last night," I replied, backing off warily.

"Come on, don't be a wimp," she responded. "Last night was an accident. Besides, this is different."

"OK, but be careful," I warned, extending my right arm.

With the cuff secured just above my elbow and the stethoscope under it, she began pumping the rubber bulb to inflate the band. As it swelled, the Velcro fastener cracked and creaked under the strain.

The cuff is attached to a column of mercury which climbs up a tube with numbers on it as the pressure in the band increases. When it is high enough, a valve is released which decreases the pressure and causes the column of mercury to drop in the tube. At the same time, the person taking your blood pressure listens for a heartbeat through the stethoscope and then reads the appropriate number from the tube. The number that is read at the first heartbeat is the high pressure, and the number that is read at the last heartbeat is the low pressure. Hence, we get readings like 120 over 80, and so on. It sounds simple, and it is. Usually.

However, before a person can do something well, a lot of practice is often required, and blood pressure reading is no exception. The first heartbeat comes through the stethoscope suddenly, and, in the case of the novice, it is easy to miss the reading on the scale.

As soon as the future nurse realized she had missed the reading, she closed the pressure valve and pumped up the cuff a second time. She also missed on this try, so she pumped up the cuff again. Same on the third attempt, and the fourth, and the fifth, and so on. It is important to keep in mind that during all of these attempts the blood flow in my arm remained restricted, so that after a dozen or so 'pump-ups', I was becoming gravely concerned.

"Darling," I said, "are you sure . . . ."

"Shush! I'm concentrating!" she shot back, her eyes focused on the tube with the intensity of a NASA space technician during a shuttle launch. *Grin and bear it*, I thought.

Pump . . . pump . . . pump.

"Sweetheart, please . . . ." I groaned as a funny sensation moved through my hands and fingers.

Pump . . . pump . . . pump.

By this time my arm was starting to feel as if it were being pinched in two. Beads of sweat had formed on my forehead, waves of nausea had swept over me, and my finger tips had turned blue. I prayed fervently.

Pump . . . pump . . . pump.

"Darling," I pleaded, "don't you think you should sto . . . ."

"Shut up! I almost got it that time."

Pump . . . pump . . . pump.

The blue in my fingers had moved into my wrist. The veins in my forearm were bulging, as though they had overdosed on steroids. A burning sensation shot through my arm which caused me to panic. I jumped back, clawing at the cuff, and stepped on the cat's tail. The animal attacked me again and left a six-inch gash on the calf of my left leg and two tooth prints on the big toe of my right foot. I lost my balance and banged my right elbow on the corner of the desk as I fell to the floor.

The next evening I sat in my special chair nursing a second gauze-wrapped calf and another banged-up elbow, also in a sling. As I sat there, I looked like a man whose spirit was all but broken. Except for slow blinking, all body movements caused pain.

"Dave, come and see what I brought home!" the future Florence called out excitedly.

Something told me not to go, but, in agony, I hobbled to the room. I stood in the doorway and looked at this woman who wanted to dedicate her life to relieving pain and suffering. Then I saw it.

"Don't you dare touch me with that thing!" I yelled as I stepped backwards. I began to tremble, with panic rising inside, sweat forming outside.

"It's all right, I just wanted to show it to you," she said, moving toward me.

"Stay away from me!" I yelled.

As she came closer, shock waves surged through every fibre of my frame which caused the production of enough adrenaline to help me overcome my injuries and to run screaming from the house. I bolted down the street, both arms restricted in their movement because of the slings. Four feet of gauze bandage trailed behind each leg. Sweat flew off my forehead and splashed onto the pavement. Our neighbours' houses had a curious head in every window wondering what had finally possessed the strange and unpredictable Elliott who lived up the road.

Meanwhile, the future nurse was left feeling a little puzzled as she stood alone in the room, innocently clutching a catheter kit!

A Busted Wire
Janalee A. Strowbridge

We stood apart
like a severed wire
ripped at its seam:
a forceful power surge
inside our covering
struck our veins,
separating us.
We fuse at each other's rip;
once we carried a purpose,
now we share the scar,
coming together again
to connect
and be as one.

The Flood
Stacey M. Hiscock

There was a fire
Started by our passionate, burning love;
The tears you left behind stopped it—
That's what started the flood.

A Castaway
Daphne Russell

Baby! Do you want a love song
I can whisper in your ear?
Maybe just a rock and roll song.
Or do you really care?

I've tried so hard to please you.
Do the things you want me to.
But, darling, you ignore me,
No matter what I do.

It hurts me so much, honey,
When I don't fit in your plans.
My heart just breaks inside.
It's hard for me to understand.

You never say you love me
With a small kiss on the cheek.
You never give me just a smile.
I tremble when you speak.

You are so cold; you do not care.
If you only would say
You love me and you need me,
That I'm not a castaway.

Opposite Agendas
Marilyn Young

They fast become friends as
Commitments and similar likes
Draw them together.

Hours pass as they
Spend time discussing their
Views, opinions,
Most times agreeing,
Not always.

Still, it is different with each other—
No condemnation, no reprisals,
For caring, for giving
So much of themselves.

Then, like a silent killer,
The first flickers of more than
Just friendship
Drive them to consider more
Time together.

Then he begins to retreat—feeling
Trapped, yet pushed to places he
Cannot allow himself to go,
To have feelings he cannot let himself hold.

She, understanding more of what is
Happening, wants the connection
But not the involvement.

Like a hermit, he hides,
Sheltered by barriers he creates,
While she waits alone
To wonder why.

Two of a Kind
Janalee A. Strowbridge

We collided
like two sharp stones
thrown together in harsh encounter,
scraping, grinding
each other's surface
until we shaped each other
in an embrace
and a relationship was born.

You
Sarah Penney-Flynn

Your memory haunts my heart,
like the crushed petals of a rose,
withered and crumbling between the pages of a book,
and yet the phantom of its scent lingers between
the living prose found there.
And I wonder if it's your face I see in the shadows of my
restless, empty dreams —
with morning-glory eyes that flicker amber in the
candlelight,
so that I cannot tell whether they beckon or banish me.
Is it your voice I hear in the lull of the waves as
they cradle the rocks?
How can I tell if it's your touch when a supple branch
bends,
to brush its leaves along my skin?
Do you wish upon the same star as I do—the third one
from the right—
and bathe your face in the same moon finger,
its liquid silver upon your cheek?
Do you want to stretch you arms to the clouds,
like the branches of a cypress on a craggy cliff by the
sea—
to touch the clouds with your fingertips,
to dance with the wind's intoxicating embrace,
to find your lullaby in the siren's lilting voice?
Or are you like a periwinkle's empty shell—
devoid of the spirit I seek?
Or the aloof richness of an orchid—
when I need the simplicity of a rose?

Return to Bliss
Edith C. Johnson

When Lizbeth Talbert opened the front door of her large, old house the phone was ringing, shrill and insistent. She dropped her bag and keys on the hall table and lifted the receiver to her ear.

"Hello," said Paul in his dignified voice. "Where have you been? I was about to hang up."

"The hairdresser's," she replied, glancing in the gilt-framed mirror above the telephone. Her short hair was blown dry around her perfectly oval face. She always wore it that way now; it was the latest style. It suited the fashionable woman she had become.

"I'll be late tonight," Paul said. "In fact, I may not be home 'til tomorrow. I have to go out of town."

"Oh!" Lizbeth sat on the red velour chair, kicked off her high-heeled shoes and wriggled her toes. "We're supposed to be going to a party at Sari's tonight. Had you forgotten about it?"

"Sari's? Yes, I had forgotten. Sorry, but it can't be helped." He didn't sound sorry. There was a little excitement in his voice.

"What's happened, Paul? Has it to do with that takeover business you told me about a few days ago?"

"I haven't time to explain now. My plane's scheduled to leave in a minute."

"But Paul . . . ."

"I must go now. Good-bye, Lizbeth."

There was a click and then the dial tone. Slowly she replaced the receiver and stared at it for a moment. She felt a chill of loneliness. Oh, Paul, she thought sadly, at one

148

time would you ever have let me party without you?

She took a cigarette from the silver case in her bag and lit it. Her curiosity wasn't really aroused by Paul's unexpected trip—as part of management of a paper company he spent a lot of time travelling—but by the excitement she had sensed in him. It was longer than she cared to admit since she had last heard that enthusiastic lilt in his voice.

Lizbeth looked around her at the outward signs of her husband's success. Suddenly she knew with dreadful, final certainty that she hated it all. Hated not only the expensive luxury of the house but the way of life it represented—their way of life. They could afford so much now, even if success allowed for a private boarding school for their daughter, Cynthia.

Slowly she went up the curving staircase. Her nylon stocking feet made no sound on the thick carpet. The hushed, listening silence of the house pressed around her. At the landing window she paused, looking out over the small green garden and the blue pond across the path. A few children were playing there. Her attention was caught by a girl wearing pink slacks and a white blouse, bending over a pram. As Lizbeth watched, the girl lifted her baby to her, kissing its soft cheeks. The girl's long hair fell forward, enclosing the two of them in a private world of love. Lizbeth turned quickly from the window, shocked by a sudden feeling of jealousy.

She would feel better after she called Sari. She tapped her long fingernails as the rings went through.

Finally, Sari's drowsy voice drawled over the line. "Whoever you are, why can't you call at a respectable hour?" Her voice rose resentfully. "Don't you know it's the middle of the night?"

"This is Lizbeth and," she added quietly, "the time is half-past eleven in the morning."

"Oh!" There was a long pause. Lizbeth could imagine Sari squirming up among her frilly pink pillows to squint in disbelief at the bedside clock. "So it is," she conceded. In a faint voice she said, "I think I'm about to die."

"Serves you right," Lizbeth replied. Sari led a life of reckless, almost hysterical, gaiety, and she seldom went to bed before dawn.

"I can't think of why I like you," Sari replied bitterly. "You're more attractive than I am, which I find hard to forgive. And you are not very sympathetic."

"Well, in that case, it will please you to know that we can't come tonight."

"Tonight? What's on tonight?"

"You're having a cocktail party," Lizbeth reminded her, "but we won't be there. Paul just called. He has to go out of town and may not be back until tomorrow."

"That doesn't mean you can't come, does it? I need you. Attractive women stop men from talking in shop corners."

"You know I detest going to parties without Paul."

"Oh, really, Lizbeth, do show a little intelligence. Men don't like a clinging vine these days."

Lizbeth glanced again at her reflection in the mirror. It would be a pity to waste a brand new hair-do. Paul's implied indifference on the phone still irritated her.

"All right," she agreed a little ungraciously. "I'll come for a little while."

"Good." Sari just failed to disguise the edge of malice in her voice as she added, "Darling, after all, who knows what that gorgeous husband of yours is up to on this sudden trip? You may as well have a fling, too."

After Lizbeth had replaced the receiver, Sari's mocking voice continued to echo unpleasantly in her ears. For an instant she remained motionless. Her eyes wandered slowly around the very pretty hall, spacious and high-ceilinged. The colours were "decorators' colours" of red and gold. The furniture was graceful in design. Expensive rugs provided bright colours on the dark, polished floor. The scent of fresh-cut flowers drifted through the quiet air. She had to move about.

She hesitated outside Cynthia's room, opened the door softly, then went in. The room smelled stale from disuse and it looked unnaturally tidy. An orderly row of dolls on the shelf stared vacantly into space. No sign of Cynthia was to be seen—Cynthia with her bright tresses and quick, infectious laughter.

Lizbeth leaned against the door, and the longing for her child gathered in a choking lump in her throat. She closed the door of the neatly arranged room and went into her own bedroom. She lay on the bed and closed her eyes and remembered how life had been.

That was ten years ago. A lifetime! They had been so young—Paul twenty-two, she barely twenty—when they got married. They had been so eager to fulfil all their hopes and dreams.

Paul had been an ambitious, intelligent young man, and he had worked hard to achieve the position he now held. With success had come a new standard of living and a new way of life. They had sold their little house in the country, with its lilac bushes, fresh air, quiet streets, lazily busy people. They had come to live in this tall, graceful old house in Montreal. Cynthia had been taken out of the local day school and enrolled in an exclusive boarding school in Toronto.

Paul and Lizbeth now went to smart parties and dined out in famous and expensive restaurants. Their friends were amusing and lively; they were also bored, neurotic and confused—they danced, drank, and divorced one another as they searched greedily for happiness. It seemed like only yesterday that Paul had whispered, "I'll love you forever." In happier days, they used to sleep in each other's arms, secure in their love. Nowadays, they slept in twin beds, and there were sleeping pills in the bathroom cabinet.

They seldom discussed their friends, no longer shocked by the things they did in their pursuit of pleasure. In fact, on the rare occasions when Paul and Lizbeth did spend an evening alone by the fireplace, they each were secretly dismayed to find that they had very little to talk about. Before, silence between them had been a thing of warmth and intimacy and easy companionship; now it was a cold void.

Lizbeth got up from the bed. She stared out the window at the smog hanging over the city and thought: how he has changed! She knew that she had changed, too—outwardly. I spend my days acting, she thought. I'm another mother who is too busy to bring up her own child. I'm the poised, charming hostess, listening attentively, laughing, yearning in secret.

She sat back on the bed and her eyes grew dreamy as she remembered the summer days in the garden of their little country house, the smell of the flowers and newly-mown grass, and the feel of sun-warmed earth in her hands.

One Sunday afternoon, Cynthia had helped her transplant flowers and pull out the weeds, while Paul was mowing the lawn. Suddenly Paul had grabbed Cynthia and dumped her in a barrow full of grass. Cynthia had squealed with delight as Paul wheeled her off and tipped her into the heap of lawn cuttings underneath the apple tree in a corner of the garden.

"Mummy, save me!" Cynthia had yelled, and Lizbeth had ended up in the lawn cuttings, too, with Cynthia frolicking wildly while Paul held Lizbeth prisoner in the soft, freshly-cut grass. He had laughed down at Lizbeth. Then the laughter had gone from his eyes and she had blushed and glanced at Cynthia, as though the little girl could have understood the look that passed between her parents. Paul released Lizbeth and helped her up. She had gone back to her flowers, basking in a glow of loving and being loved.

As Lizbeth thought of it now her eyes filled with tears. There had been no such times in this house. She had always loved friends and laughter, but now she lived a different, lonely life.

She stood up and put away her memories from the past, feeling ashamed of herself and, in a way, even feeling disloyal to Paul. Wasn't this what he had worked so hard to attain? Wasn't this the sort of life they had both wanted?

Lizbeth knew the moment she arrived what Sari's party was going to be like. I won't stay long, she promised herself; I'll go home and go to bed early. Pausing for a moment at the door, she listened to the stridency of the guests' chatter. She watched the crowd, amused by the realization that if they never saw each other again, most of them would not care in the least.

A tide of perfume followed Sari to Lizbeth's side. Sari was in her element, with a drink in one hand and an admiring and attractive man at her elbow. Her red, sheer voile dress would have been revealing had she not been so thin. Her slender arms were loaded with a jangling collection of bracelets.

"Hello, darling." Sari kissed the smoky air beside Lizbeth's cheek. "I'm so glad you came. Isn't this chaos?"

Lizbeth was drawn quickly into the crowd. She greeted people she knew and sipped a drink she didn't like. Someone said, "Lizbeth, my sweet, this is Egbert Sniffen. He's been badgering everyone for an introduction ever since you arrived."

With the ease of long practice, the man called Egbert Sniffen manoeuvred Lizbeth away into a corner, effectively blocking her escape by leaning one well-tailored shoulder against the wall. He poured flattery over her like syrup, and as he spoke his eyes never left her face.

Lizbeth felt a sense of dislike prickle and crawl over her skin as the predator moved a little closer. "I expect you're aware that you are very beautiful," he breathed.

"Oh, yes, I know," Lizbeth said politely. "I'm unusual too."

Sniffen looked more closely at this blonde-haired woman, noting the delicate beauty of her skin. "Unusual?" he replied with a smile.

"Yes. In fact, you might almost say that I'm a freak in these circles. You see, I've been married to the same man for ten years and I like it." Then she slid past his arm and was gone.

She made her way swiftly across the room to the corner where Sari was standing. "But, darling, do you have to go now?" Sari shrieked. "This is going to be a splendid evening. I don't suppose I'll be able to get rid of them until morning." Lizbeth kissed Sari's thin, flushed cheek in a sudden rush of pity for her. As she left the room, Lizbeth noticed that Egbert Sniffen was already stalking his next quarry.

When she stepped from the taxi that brought her home, she saw lights streaming from her living room windows, casting black bars of shadow across the pavement as they shone through the railings. Before she had time to find her keys Paul opened the door. Lizbeth's heart skipped a beat when she saw her husband standing there holding the door for her. "Hello. So you got back then," she said idiotically.

He bent and kissed her cheek automatically. Her question required no answer. His voice was preoccupied as he asked, "Did you have a good time?" She glanced at him, puzzled. She found that he was watching her, his expression searching, intent. He dropped his eyes and turned away.

"Have you had anything to eat?" she enquired, following him into the living room.

"Come sit down, Lizbeth. I have something I must tell you." He mixed them a drink, his face troubled and strained.

Sudden icy fingers of fear clutched Lizbeth's heart as Sari's words came back to her: "Who knows what that gorgeous husband of yours is up to on this sudden trip?" Oh, no! she cried silently. Not us, not Paul and me! We've drifted apart, perhaps, but we still love each other; we still belong together.

Paul handed her the drink. She cradled the glass between her palms, gazing down into it. She watched the tiny bubbles rise to the surface, only to burst and vanish.

"Lizbeth?"

With an effort she stopped watching the bubbles rising in her glass and looked up. I love you, she thought, but I've lost you.

He was speaking. "You know I told you some time ago that there was a take-over bid for the company. Well, it has all been signed and sealed. We are to amalgamate with a much bigger company and they want me to stay on and run the whole thing."

She tried to force her mind to make some sense of what he was telling her. He hadn't found someone else. Blood sang in her ears, and she felt light-hearted with relief.

He asked, "Do you understand what I'm saying?"

"Yes, oh, yes. You—you must be very pleased."

"You know that I have a lot of shares in the company."

"Shares?" She tried to sound knowledgeable. "Shares? Oh, yes, I know."

"If I want I can sell out. We'd have quite a lot of money."

She forced herself to pay attention. "But, Paul, you've worked so hard. It's been your life."

"That's just the trouble."

"What do you mean?"

He lit a cigarette. After a moment he said, "At one time you would never have gone to a party by yourself. And you would have disliked a woman like Sari with her cheap boyfriends."

"If you left the company and sold your shares, what

would you do?"

He got up and began to pace around the room. He came to a halt in front of her. His expression was a confused mixture of defiance and pleading.

"Lizbeth, today I went down to Heatherton to look at a farm, just a small farm. I want to buy it and raise pedigree Jersey cows."

"Oh," she said, stunned. "Do you know anything about pedigree cows?"

"No. But I've made a success of one job; I can make a success of another."

They stared at each other in silence for a moment. Then he added, "Lizbeth, I want to get away from the city and from what it is doing to our marriage. I want to have Cynthia with us again."

Tears began to slide down her cheeks, making dark splashes on the rich brocade of the sofa. His handkerchief
touched her hand.

"It's all right, darling," he soothed. "Nothing has been settled. I told them that I must talk to you first. It's your life, too." Paul tried to muffle the disappointment in his voice. "I think I knew, really, when you came in just now. You've changed so much; you look so right, so at home, in this setting. It would be unfair to ask you to move to Heatherton." He leaned down and tilted Lisbeth's troubled face to meet his gaze.

"Paul," she said, "I want to get away from here. I want a garden with a lawn, lilac bushes and flowers." As he drew her into his arms with a passionate, protecting gesture, she asked, "Could you do it without regrets?"

The deep glow of the smile kindled behind his eyes gave Lizbeth her answer.

From Whence We Came:

Remembering the Past, Creating the Future

Cabot's Prize
Daphne Russell

Five centuries ago Cabot left Bristol shores,
In search of a land that was free.
He sailed on the Matthew for many long days,
Then finally land he could see.
Everything looked loving and peaceful;
Bonavista the place they did land.
A prize that would make England's king so proud:
New founde landes, now called Newfoundland.

Our forefathers came to make a new home,
Work the land and fish the deep sea.
England claimed this island, all for its own—
Made New founde landes their own colony.
We are caring and proud Newfoundlanders;
We will welcome you in for a tea.
Won't you come and join us as we celebrate
The discovery that means life to me.

There's a mixed race of folk here in Newfoundland,
With hearts made of gold, and we care—
So please come along as we sing our songs,
Bring your flags—we'll fly them everywhere.
We have oh-so-much to be proud of:
Lots of mountains and streams and fresh air;
We have our own songs, jigs and reels you'll enjoy—
Come along for our five-hundredth year.

Manchester Soldier
Brian J. Hoskins

Across the Autumn Square the veterans stand,
Bereted, blue-blazered, most noble band.
The crowd shuffles and stares with a curious air,
Glimpsing the men who are standing there.
One soldier remembers sadly his glories past,
His many young friends who had fought to the last.
But to his wearied mind comes most of all
Those nights in Manchester before the call.
Fifty years have not dulled his mind
Of how charming she was and how very kind.
Through dark August streets and by the factory wall—
A lonesome young girl and a soldier on call.
Her name was Connie, she had quietly said,
Just a Manchester girl, not looking to wed.
And would a young soldier-boy, with so far to roam,
Be so kind as to see a girl home?
But falling in love beneath an English moon
Came far too easy and much too soon.
To each other, they would secrets impart,
Pretending in vain he would never depart.
He recalled her softness that scented night,
As a frightened young soldier before the great fight.
But as lonely hearts great wars make,
They became lost in each other, for loneliness' sake.
His memory aches with a yearning despair
To those nights in Manchester, none can compare.
Arm in arm down the old Oxford Road,
Heart in heart, unburdening their load.
Nights of warm promises and hot Pekoe tea,

Days of azure by the great Irish Sea—
As if in secret, amid the war gloom,
They had quietly found their own Brigadoon.
Then hastily one night he was summoned away
To the continent, to war—a maddening day.
A note scribbled quickly to his girl was sent:
Would she please call him, at the war's end?
Now as he shuffles his feet in this November air,
His broken heart pleads that he never did care.
But a wounded heart fights a war of its own;
For when true love is given, it is never on loan.
The nearby crowd jostles and presses to see
The motley old crew in that blue-blazered sea.
But the cost of war, hurried youth never knows,
Nor can number the hearts broken, in those weary rows.
Throughout the town square, the bugles resound,
Rekindling the memories of those gathered 'round.
But one man remembers war's costly extremes,
And sighs in his sadness, at his Manchester dreams.

The Train
Terry G. Manuel

She came early in the morning,
blowing her whistle.

I miss hearing that whistle blow,
jumping on her for a ride down Main Street,
jumping off by the station.

Then she would go on her way,
maybe come back later on—
another ride down Main Street.

But now she's gone,
The Train.

Why the Newfie Bullet Went Bang . . .
Ronald T. Smith

A couple of Sundays ago, in a westerly gale, I huddled at the CN train station with nearly one hundred others in an effort to savour a final taste of the atmosphere of the Newfoundland Rail Road before it whistled its way into the annals of the province's history. The crowd, consisting mainly of Deer Lakers, contained a surprising number of children anxious to ride the fabled railway in order to cement their own place in Newfoundland history and to pass it on to yet another generation to come.

True to performance, the train, led by locomotive 927 and backed up by 946, chugged into town twenty-five minutes late. An uncertain crowd continued to brave the biting wind while a throng of Gaff Topsail cabin owners disembarked. Two passenger cars, with a total capacity of eighty people, had been filled, and it was clear that all those waiting could not be boarded. Earlier, in the train station, a waiting line had dispersed when the agent refused to issue more tickets.

While train officials determined the number of passengers to be accommodated, and adults and children continued to shuffle in the chilling wind, everything but the kitchen sink was offloaded by the cabin owners, who, no doubt sensing the immediate demise of the railway, seized the opportunity to bring back beds and other furniture from cabins accessible only by the railway.

Groups formed at each of the passenger cars. A train hand caused a stir when he said that perhaps nobody would be taken on. Reacting to objections from the crowd, all with tickets purchased, he explained that people had been left at Bishop's Falls and none had been taken aboard at Grand Falls. A confrontation between the more demanding in the crowd and the train crew drew little positive results. "You should have put more cars on. You knew the tickets were being sold. You should have known this was going to happen," charged an irate would-be passenger, waving his ticket over his head. "Where are all the cars? In St. John's? Where they can use them?"

"That," returned a train hand flatly, "is not my problem. Although it could be yours."

Finally, after another twenty minutes, it was announced that ten from our group would be accepted. Luckily, with camera in hand and pen behind my ear, I made it. But let me assure you, there was no preference, media or otherwise. It was simply because I had shuffled into the right place at the right time. Something like a lottery or a spot dance.

Days of Glamour Gone

Inside the train, I receive my first shock. The glamour of the railway apparently had begun to diminish decades ago, just after my last train ride. It would have taken that long to degrade any system to its current state. The era of well-upholstered passenger cars, smokers where one might play cards or chat and imbibe, dining cars with real linen tablecloths and sterling silver, sleeping quarters with porters and immaculately dressed conductors have vanished as surely as the shrill of the whistle would.

Sadly, it has been replaced with a transportation system only the few and the desperate would use, even if the railway were to last a hundred years more.

The cars are painted a dingy gray. The central

heating system has been replaced with a couple of oil stoves at either end of a car, with pipes protruding through the ceiling. Many of the seats, in either blue or red, are in disrepair. The floor is one great ashtray; the tiny cubicle called a washroom is also painted a dingy gray. There is an antique white porcelain toilet bowl with a foot plunger. A soggy half-roll of toilet paper sits on a tiny steel wash basin. There is no paper in the hanger, but a full roll lies out near the stove. There is cold water only.

Finally, at 4:00 p.m., an hour behind a schedule no one any longer seems to care about, the train pulls out of Deer Lake. Getting on is rough, but is a picnic compared to what happens at the end of the journey.

But the nostalgic sense of 'train' is gripping as the two locomotives speed up and you slip—bouncing, jumping and rolling—past Deer Lake, through Spillway and St. Judes, and westward with a click-clack most Newfoundlanders have grown up with.

Even the dilapidated condition of the train cannot erase the beauty of an angle of the countryside that can be seen only by rail. Trees are plentiful. Horses are in the fields and there a farmer waves at us as we roll by. To the left, entering Little Harbour, the lake is furious with white caps whipped by the strong westerly wind.

Slipping back in time, I think the cars must have been bigger. But that could not have been so, considering the narrow gauge track. The conductor brings the time back quickly. He is not the snappy polished conductor I knew, the figure of authority with the immaculate suit, peaked round hat and gleaming gold buttons. Now he wears a black work shirt, a pair of jeans and a cap with a common logo. Similarly, he lacks any sense of authority.

The Newfoundland Railway appears not to be high on women's liberation. There never was a female conductor. And now there never will be.

System Out of Whack

Something happens now to confirm that the system is a little out of whack. A passenger in the next seat informs the conductor that he doesn't have a ticket. Instead he offers the conductor cash for the fare, which is readily and politely accepted. But what about all those people at the Deer Lake station with tickets who could not get on the train?

We continue to sweep through the magnificent scenery of the Humber Valley. Through a window that has been pierced at one time with a pellet gun, I see the beginning of autumn, as the leaves change and begin their annual riot of colour. The sun slants through a dusty window, casting prisms of light on the bouncing interior.

In an adjacent compartment, a young lady wearing fashion glasses and a mauve sweater with lipstick to match, casually pops a Blue from a case underneath her seat. To the left, Pasadena Beach appears, sandy and windswept, and then recedes into the forest.

We slip into South Brook Park and surge past trailers in camping lots. Then, a surprise, but not one welcomed later. A train hand in jeans and a green windbreaker with another common logo emblazoned on the jacket breast and a portable telephone strapped to his belt asks us if we will need a taxi in Corner Brook. Indeed we do . . . and thank him for his courtesy.

We relax to the smell of burning diesel, whiffs of smoke mingling with the crisp autumn air, and . . . 'train'.

167

At Elizabeth Drive we see the backs of new luxurious homes and people waving from patio doors. Nearing Steady Brook, a light mist begins to fall and a rainbow materializes, with the proverbial pot of gold somewhere on the other side of the lake.

Lights Flash By

Red crossing lights flash by, and soon we enjoy a panoramic view of majestic Marble Mountain, at the moment devoid of snow yet splendid in the pristine atmosphere of autumn. To our right flows the tranquil Humber River.

We slip through Humbermouth. People in cars stopped at Brake's Cove Crossing wave, and kids return their greeting. A man in a white shirt waves from his window. The announcement comes that we are arriving at Humbermouth Station. There is a flurry of activity, and we can see a number of cabs waiting. But we are going to Corner Brook, are we not?

Fifteen minutes later a train hand reports that we will be continuing to the city. A quarter of a mile from our destination we stop and the locomotives are disconnected. The train hand explains that we will be brought in by shunter.

Why the Bullet Journey Went Bang

The journey stops at the extremity of the Corner Brook harbour development. It is raining, and there is no railway station or any cabs in sight. "What happened to the taxi?" I ask a train hand as we prepare to disembark. "They were in Humbermouth. Should have got off there," he replies. A train hand announces that this is where the train will be "made up" for the return trip and that if we want return passage, we should be here "about 8:30 p.m."

With women and children in tow, we disembark. The nearest telephone is up Station Road and down Main Street to Hotel Corner Brook. Walking up that hill, toting a camera case, and being drenched by sheets of rain driven relentlessly by a strong westerly gale, I suddenly realized why the Newfie Bullet went bang.

Huffing, puffing and soaked, we weave and stumble to the hotel where telephones, taxis and more are waiting. Undaunted, we are prepared to make the return trip. Returning at the appointed hour, we think we have missed the train but breathe a sigh of relief as it shunts back to its departure position.

The return trip is better. Could it be because darkness has enveloped the entire scenario? A beautiful harvest moon dances through the clouds.

The shaft of a guitar protrudes through the opening of the adjacent compartment, and the sounds of "The Wild Rover" and "Blowing in the Wind" are muted as the train picks up speed. Near Pasadena the accordion comes on stream with "The Squid Jiggin' Ground."

The train lurches and a fire extinguisher pops out of its strapping. The train hand shrugs and kicks it under a seat.

Devastation Too Great

I lie back, stretch out and savour the end of an era. But as the nostalgic click-clack draws me closer to home, I wonder if I would ever use the system again, even if it stayed for another hundred years. Considering the options of a comfortable car on a paved highway or a sleek jet boarding through a modern terminal, I doubted it.

Somehow, the Newfie Bullet just didn't seem to be a part of the 80's. Not like Via Rail. The devastation is too great.

On the return trip we take our three-year-old grandson Stephen for his first and last ride on the Newfoundland Railway. Just to give him his niche in history. He enjoys it. Pity that he will never ride another train in his own province.

When September ended, so did the train whistle. Now. not even the faintest echo of it can be heard.

First published in <u>The Lakeside Press</u>, October 7, 1989.

Coming Back into this Magical World
Terry G. Manuel

This is an excerpt from <u>Walking into Paradise</u>. Terry G. Manuel's real-life experience tells of his journey back after brain injuries caused by a brutal beating in Toronto.

I woke up in the hospital where strangers stood above me, their mouths moving, making sounds that had no meaning. I closed my eyes.

"Terry, are you awake?" a voice asked.

I felt the pain of something in my throat. What was it—tubes? I tried to pull the tubes out, but couldn't. Something was holding my hands. The pain was terrible. I wanted it to go away. And questions. Everybody asking questions!

"Terry, do you know who you are? Nod your head if you do."

I closed my eyes. Why wouldn't they leave me alone? I wanted to sleep; that was a way to get away from them. But I kept opening my eyes.

Voices kept jabbering at me, "Terry, are you awake? Terry, do you know who you are?"

"No, you mustn't. No, no, Terry; don't try to pull the tubes out. No, no."

"Do you know who this is?" Do you recognize what I'm holding? Nod your head if you do."

I wished they would shut up. Slowly the faces came into focus, but I still didn't understand the noises they were making. I would look at these mouths taking on different shapes as they opened and closed. Faces moving backward and forward, fading in and out, conversations around me, strangers all around me.

Everyone was a stranger. But there was one voice I was getting used to.

"Hi, Terry. How are you? You're looking better. I'm here with you now. Do you know who I am? I'm your sister. I'm Judy, and I'm here with you. You're going to be all right."

What was all right? I had no idea what she meant. Time seemed endless, the questions were endless . . . .

"What is your name?"

"Do you recognize me?"

"Nod your head if you understand me."

I refused to nod for these silly people. I didn't know who they were, and I didn't care. For that matter, I didn't know who I was and I didn't care. I couldn't talk with all the tubes in my nose and throat anyway. Why did they keep bothering me?

One day a doctor took a tube out of my throat. "I think we'll see if he can get along without the respirator."

I was so glad to have it out that I tried to talk, but all that came out of my mouth were weird sounds. Soon I was gasping for breath and the doctor was forcing the respirator back down my throat. I tried to stop him. I didn't want that pain again. The doctor won.

In a few days the respirator was removed again. This time, it stayed out. Now I could talk. At first, I could only babble like a baby, but then, suddenly, I could say a few words that people understood. I liked seeing their amazement.

"He's coming around," said the doctors. "He understands. That's great."

"Do you know where you are?" someone asked.

"No. Am I supposed to?"

"You're in the hospital. You're going to be all right."

There were those words "all right" again. I still didn't know what they meant.

"Do you know where you live?"

"No. Am I supposed to?"

A nurse was leaning over me. "Hello. What's your name?"

"I don't know. What's your name?"

"I'm Nurse Nelson. Now, tell me your name."

"Go to hell!"

One person had the right idea. He always came in with a smile. "Hi, Terry. You're Terry Manuel, and I'm Dr. Moulton. How is Terry Manuel today?"

I liked him. He didn't try to make me remember who I was—he told me. And if he thought I was Terry Manuel, well, that was good enough for me—especially since it seemed to make him happy.

Terry Manuel, Terry Manuel. At first, I thought it was all one word. I would say it in a rush, "TerryManuel."

But the woman called Judy confused me. She kept calling me "Terry." At first, it was fun showing off that I could speak, even if none of it made sense. But, eventually, the game became tiring. I got tired of the same old questions.

"Do you know who I am?"

"Where do you live?"

Did I know this or what that was for? When I did give the right name, they showed me a clock.

I could point out the numbers on it: "That's a four and that's a six and that's a nine."

"What do you call it?"

"I don't know."

"It's a time clock."

"Do you know what time it is?"

"What's time?"

"Can you tell time with a clock?"

They explained it to me, and I re-learned it very quickly.

What did I know? What could I do? That's what the doctors wanted to know. I could speak. I could read words—but I still had to keep asking what so many things meant. At least I knew how to ask a question. Sometimes, I even understood their explanation. But why did they have to talk so fast? I started to remember faces but still I couldn't remember names—sometimes, not even my own.

"Hi, Terry, I'm here again. I'm Judy, your sister. Do you remember me now?"

I just looked at her.

"I'm Judy," she repeated. "What's your name?"

"I'm Judy," I rasped.

"No," she said, "you're Terry. I'm Judy. You're my brother Terry. Say it, Terry. Say it, Terry!"

I didn't want to say it. "I don't know you," I lashed out. "Shut up, bitch! Get out!"

I could see that she was hurt, and it pleased me. She left. But she came back the next day. Sometimes I was happy and wanted to listen to her. Other times, I was upset and shouted curses. Now I knew how to get rid of all those people standing around my bed, looking at me sadly or with forced smiles. I would just throw a tantrum. I swore at those smiling faces—the doctors, the nurses, my sister—everyone who kept telling me of his or her love.

"Damn you!" I said. "Shut up!"

Judy apologized to a nurse for my language, and she

laughed, saying, "Cursing is not at all uncommon for head injury patients. Often such patients behave in such a manner from a concussion, screaming obscenities. Your brother will get over it, Miss Manuel."

Judy said she had never heard me swear like this and was relieved that it wouldn't last forever. Sometimes the doctors laughed. Sometimes they said, "There, there. That's not nice, is it?"

"Damn bastard."

Judy would not react so mildly. She would look hurt, stricken. I was glad. Maybe now they would stay away and quit tormenting me with all those questions. "Do you remember this or do you remember that?"

"Get out, get out, son of a . . . ."

"Better let him cool down," a nurse would butt in. "Perhaps he shouldn't have this much company."

But no matter what I did, the woman they called Judy kept coming back. Why?

With the IV out of my arm, I was now feeding myself. I picked up food with my fingers, stuffed it into my mouth. The nurses urged me to take more. I didn't know why I should bother pleasing them, but sometimes I did it anyway.

One day a nurse brought in a tray with something ugly on it. "What is it, worms?" I grabbed it with my hand.

The nurse told me, "It's spaghetti," while she wiped my hand and handed me a fork.

I threw the spaghetti on the floor. "Get out, bitch."

She ran out of the room.

Now, the other one was coming in. "Get the hell out, miss," I hissed.

"I'm your nurse, remember?"

"Who the hell cares. Get out, get out!"

"I'll get the doctor."

"Shut up, shut up, shut up!" I wanted to drown out the voices.

The doctor came, patted my hand, smiled at me. I calmed down and smiled back.

He said, "For a time, it might be better if he only sees his sister and gets used to her."

"That's a good idea."

In a way I understood; they were going to do something about the people and if Dr. Moulton said so, it was all right. But I didn't want Dr. Moulton to stop paying attention to me. I let out a string of swearing.

"Now, Terry Manuel," he said; "now, now, quiet down."

In the fourth month with the tubes out I had become ambulatory and soon I was here, there and everywhere exploring this magical world. Bells rang, walls opened and closed. People appeared and disappeared. One day, a wall opened and I wheeled myself in. A door closed and I was caged in a box. Suddenly it moved. I was so scared. The door opened. I got out of there as fast as my wheelchair could move. I almost bumped into some people when I came out of that box. Finally I was found and returned to my floor.

A nurse showed me the elevator door and said, "No, no. Terry, don't get on the elevator unless we are with you. Do you understand?"

"Go to hell!" I shouted. "Shut up, bitch."

She knew what to do. She put a sign on the back of my wheelchair. "Return to Intensive Care, Neurosurgery, 10th Floor."

One day I wandered into the cafeteria, to look at all of

the people. For a time I sat in line with them staring at their faces, listening to what they were saying. Then I wandered off to a brightly lighted place where rows and rows of food were sitting in a long shiny box. I wheeled myself up and down putting my fingers into some of the food. I found a pretty bowl of ice cream and started eating it. I was having so much fun I didn't even notice that a crowd of people had gathered around, all talking excitedly.

"Where does he belong?"

Someone read the sign on the back of my wheelchair: "Return to Intensive Care, Neurosurgery, 10th Floor."

A doctor introduced himself and led me back to my ward. I was all confused now. I was wondering what day it was, and when did I come in here? Now I got a problem. How was I going to find out?

"Nurse, nurse, nurse. What day did I come in here?"

"Let me see," she answered. "It was May 5th."

"Well, what day is it now?"

"It is August 6th."

"Oh my God, what happened to all of the time? I was supposed to go back to work."

"Now, Terry, you can't work in the shape you're in."

"Nurse, when is that lady, Judy, coming back here?"

"Maybe she'll be in sometime today."

"Good; 'cause now I got to ask her something."

"Terry, write it down so you'll remember it."

Write it down, write it down. What's their problem? Now I know it'll give me something to talk about.

"Judy, can you tell me what happened?"

"Didn't they tell you?"

"Yes, they said that I had fallen down a stairway because I was drunk. But I don't believe them. I only had

$50 on me and that wasn't enough to get drunk on."

"Well you were drunk when you came in here. You were drunk and high on cocaine."

Then I didn't know or couldn't remember for so long what had really happened. But every day while being there I tried to remember, but I couldn't. I was so upset with the world and everything in it.

I didn't like being in a wheelchair. The doctors and nurses were trying to help, but it didn't seem as if I was getting anywhere with it, I thought. The way I looked at it was that I hadn't gone there in a wheelchair and I wasn't about to leave in one.

I started listening and doing the things they were telling me to do. It was hard. I didn't have any strength in my leg, but in time things started to come around. I used to get out of bed at night when there was no one else around and walk to the bathroom and back to my bed. One morning, I asked my doctor for a cane. Someone brought one. I started getting around with that. I used to go to a strange room where a kind lady asked all kinds of questions and played games with me. The big deal was to put a square peg into a square hole and a triangular peg into a triangular hole. The first day I failed real bad. After three or four days I finally figured it out. Then I was so amazed and happy with my new game that I couldn't be stopped from playing it over and over again. Einstein could not have felt smarter. I knew that every new thing that I learned took me closer to going home.

Next, I had to match words with pictures. This was harder then square pegs and round holes. It was so much fun learning what things looked like. My score wasn't high, but judging from the pictures there seemed to be an exciting world out there—and it made me all the more anxious to get at the real thing.

The doctor had said that when I felt okay and was no longer in pain I could go home. So when the doctor would ask, I would lie about how I felt. I would say "fine," even though the back of my head really hurt. I stopped telling him about whenever I had a headache.

Another day a nurse said, "Come, Terry, you are going to have a shower."

From the sound of her voice I knew this was going to be something new. She led me into this white tiled room. I saw this thing on the wall. I stood in front of it, not having the faintest idea who the image was before me.

"This is you, Terry," the nurse said.

Seeing my refection in the wall, I smiled. I laughed. This was me. I hardly noticed my face.

It was probably the longest shower I would ever take. The water felt so good as it washed over me. So warm and kind. It even made me forget the pain in my head. After I got out of the shower, I insisted on standing in front of the mirror again, looking at myself and wondering what had happened to me. How I came to be here like this. It was scary not knowing what had happened. I was feeling better now, and was being transferred to the Queen Elizabeth Hospital.

Home was a word that sounded like everything there was nice. I had to learn more about this place they called home. After some months had passed, the nurses told me I going home for Christmas.

The head nurse, Mrs. Silva, walked to the bus stop with me and got a ticket to put me on the bus.

"I'm going to have so much fun." Well at least I thought

it was going to be fun. I didn't know that I was going to be on the bus for three days and that wasn't much fun at all. I left on December 19th and arrived on the 22nd.

This was three days before Christmas. Oh boy, I couldn't wait. Everything was so strange when I walked into my home. There was a big tree up in the living room; it was so beautiful. It took me a few days to get to know everyone.

At times, someone asked me if I knew this one or that one. I had to say "yes"; I didn't want people to think that I didn't know anything. The day after Christmas, my daughter came to visit. I didn't really know her, but nobody knew that. I had a great time with my daughter for the few days she was there.

The day she left, a police officer came to my house looking for some money. He said that I had an outstanding fine for $500. When I asked him what it was all about, he told me. I asked him to give me a few minutes to try and borrow it. No one had any money.

"Well, I'll give you a few days to try to get it anyway," the police officer said. It's Christmas." He left. I didn't see him any more until January 1st.

Then I told him I still couldn't get the money. He said, "Well, I have to take you to jail. I'll be back later to pick you up.

I said to myself, "I'm going to jail." Wow—that's something new. I can't wait. I waited and waited. It didn't seem like the officer was going to come back, so I got the phone number and called him.

He answered, "I'll be down as soon as I get someone to fill in here."

I said, "Well, okay," and hung up. I didn't want him to

know that I was excited. I didn't know where this place was or what it was. But I wasn't going to tell anyone that. I didn't want them to think I was dumb.

It was about 11 p.m. when the officer showed up to take me to jail. He put me in the back seat of this funny-looking car with a glass case in front of me.

Then I started to wonder why I was here like this. I wouldn't ask the officer. He probably would have thought that I was stupid. I wasn't in the car for long when he pulled up by the side of a brick building. He let me out of the car; then he put handcuffs on me. I walked beside him into the building, and he locked me into this cage.

I didn't want anyone to think that I didn't know what was going on, so I didn't say anything. There was a bed there, so I lay down and went to sleep. The next morning, the guard asked me what I wanted to eat. Well, at least they were going to feed me.

I said quickly, "Give me bacon and eggs, juice and coffee."

I had a smoke but I didn't have a light. They had taken everything from me last night. I didn't say anything. I thought that's what they had to do.

The Beautiful Girls in White
Arthur Ball

To all you fair young ladies
In uniforms of white:
The career that you have chosen
Is really worth the fight.

Patients lying in their beds,
As the nurse passes gently by,
See a smile upon her face;
From her lips, a gentle sigh.

We know that God has planted
In every nurse's heart
A sympathy for sufferers,
And we know you'll do your part.

As you walk the corridors
And enter patients' rooms,
You spread a ray of sunshine
That takes away the gloom.

Your loving words and smiles
Fill patients with delight,
As you move from bed to bed
In your uniforms of white.

The Purple Rose on Mother's Grave
Daphne Russell

Our mom has gone to heaven and left us all behind.
I miss my darling mother; no comfort can I find.
I miss her love; I miss her smile, the tears she
shed with us,
standing by her bedside when she couldn't talk to us.

For two long years, she suffered; she was in so much pain.
Her eyes would fill with many tears as her energy did wane.
She would hold her hand up gently to touch us
on the face.
Each day I carry memories that nothing can erase.

Our dad would sit beside her morning, noon, and night.
He would feed her all her meals with food that
Mother liked.
Oh, how he loved and cared for her as happy as could be.
He would go home tired and weary and lonely
we could see.

Then one day he left her, telling her that he'd return.
One hour later, the sad news Dad did learn.
God quickly took her while we were all away,
deciding it was best to take her home this way.

The day we laid our mom to rest, the snow was
on the ground.
The wind was blowing very hard as they lowered
her casket down.

As I said good-bye to her before I left that day,
I placed a little purple rose on my mother's grave.

With new flowers for her birthday, to her grave
we went today.
She loved us and she loved flowers in a very special way.
There was no marker to show us—everything was
moved away;
Then suddenly I saw the faded purple rose on
Mother's grave.

Nobody's Grandmother
Nellie P. Strowbridge

We had just got inside the restaurant and sat at a table when a sign indicating that the place was closed was propped in a window.

We looked gratefully toward the young waitress who came toward us smiling an assurance. She took our order, then she quickly pocketed pen and pad. She turned to go, then she came back, an apologetic smile on her lips. "Our water pipes broke; that's why we're closed, but we can manage your order."

We settled back, relieved. A second, older waitress snapped at the younger one, "Lock the door."

She did—but it easily swung open for the next couple.

There was no gentle tone in the older waitress's voice, no apologetic explanation such as the younger waitress had given us, just a blunt "We're closed" to the elderly couple who had just stepped inside.

"Oh, I didn't know," said the woman, obviously flustered as she turned toward the door. The man opened it after sending a quick glance in the direction of more fortunate people like us.

As for the old lady sitting alone munching toast and sipping tea from a brown scenic cup, the two waitresses could have easily enjoyed her quietness. The woman seemed reluctant to get to the bottom. But the waitresses couldn't know that their patience would be tested, not until . . . .

The small bumpy woman finally stood at the counter and said in a loud voice, "I was wondering about my bill." Her Southern accent sounded conspicuous in that small

New Brunswick town.

"Your bill," explained the younger waitress, "is in the little tray on your table."

"Oh, dear me," the old lady, her hands with their long manicured and lacquered nails flittered in the air, "I must have overlooked it."

She moved angularly back to the table and secured the bill. Taking a lingering look at the little thatched-roofed house and its winding road spread serenely across the miniature tray, she sighed and set her mouth regrettably. She came back holding the bill out in both hands.

"Are you closed for today?" Her beady eyes darted to the sign, then they came back with an incredulous look. "I told myself that it is too early to be closed on Sunday. Is it?"

The young waitress started to explain, but the old lady had found another thought. "I wonder . . . ." Her eyes lit on an old-fashioned stove sitting against the wall. "How delightful! Simply an ornament, I suppose."

"Oh yes," beamed the girl. "It . . . ."

The old lady interrupted, "I had the most delicious— just the most delicious crab salad here last evening. I wonder, would you have some I could take with me?"

"I'll see," the younger waitress smiled indulgently; the older one lifted her eyes and shrugged.

Taking a little jug from a plastic bag, the old lady wondered if she could have a little water to take with her.

"I'm sorry," the older waitress said sharply.

"Wait!" called the younger one, going toward the refrigerator. "Here's a little."

The old lady's eyes lit up. "This jug is very old, you know; it was my grandmother's."

The young waitress pointed proudly to the stove and a carved high chair, "These are very old . . . ."

"Yes, yes," said the old lady absentmindedly. She spied her salad all ready to go. "Did I pay for it with my meal?" she asked penuriously.

The older waitress rolled her eyes and shook her head.

"Oh." The old lady's gnarled hand struggled with the clasp on her handbag. She offered money for the salad cautiously. Then she pulled the foil-wrapped container toward her. "I'll be back soon," she chuckled.

The young waitress smiled; the older one sighed.

The old lady was on her way to the door when a thought must have hit her. She came back. "I'm wondering," she ventured, "how old your stove and chair are."

The older waitress continued clearing the tables. She didn't look up to answer. "I don't know."

"My jug is a hundred years old. Grandma died at seventy. She's been dead for a long time . . . ." She searched the waitress's face for some interest. There was none. As she went toward the door she looked back as if to see if that 'nice' waitress would come out of the kitchen.

As we passed the old lady's car, her window was down and I heard her sigh, "I wonder did they miss me at the old folk's home?" She looked longingly at the restaurant window as if hoping for a wave good-bye. There was none, and she drove away alone, her shoulders hunched above the wheel.

Cuffs
Nellie P. Strowbridge

My mother clicked her silver needles,
weaving magic in the air,
carving diamonds in warm colours
of the land and sea.
We waited for the silence
of the needles, when new cuffs
would fit our hands in cosy comfort.
And we would leave the house to take on
winter's bite and icy glaze.
We shivered home at last
and dropped those cuffs,
heavy now with globs of ice,
from our small, damp red hands.
My mother hung those cuffs
on the white enamel warmer,
where ice dropped into pellets,
hissing and popping, on the black top stove.
It, like a hot tongue, lapped the water.
The coal stove's heat turned cuffs
into toasty-warm covers for our hands
against the next day's winter's bite.

'Twas The Day Before Christmas
David Elliott

'Twas the day before Christmas, and down at the mall
Were thousands of people, the big and the small,
To do panic shopping before the next day
And make sure that everyone got his own way.

Now, I had gone down there just like all the rest,
To purchase a gift for the one I love best;
While she's not too demanding, she likes
things of worth,
So I had to get something to keep peace on earth.

The excitement, alas, took all my attention,
And I got caught up with all the contention
Of people berserk on a mad shopping spree,
Making sure there was lots to go under the tree.

The hustle and bustle, the worry and fuss,
Would rattle a preacher and cause him to cuss;
Crowds tripping over one another that day,
Learning that tardiness just doesn't pay.

Al Bunyon was there with son, Danny, too,
Who wanted to buy his dad a pair shoes;
Now Al was so proud but let out a great moan
When Danny came to him to ask for a loan.

Art shouted to me while hot on the trot,
Said, "Come 'ere, ol' man, and see what I got
Fer mudder and fawder and young brudder, Jack":
'Twas a big bag of candy—the variety pack!

Poor Sally Harnum was all in a twitter
As she tried to find the right size of a sweater,
"To give to me 'usband," that's what she said;
"But I can't find the kind that pulls over yer 'ead."

I saw Uncle Joe Samson looking at dishes
And all sorts of other stuff good for his missus;
He was spinnin' around, so before he went wacky,
He bought his good wife twelve plugs of tabaccy.

Proud Billy Durdle with his lovely wife, Kim,
Were buying up toys for their six-year-old twin;
Said Bill, "This is not really too hard to do,
'Cause whatever we buys we times it by two!"

Poor Arthur Pritchard was very upset,
Said, "I haven't a clue 'bout what I should get
Fer d'wife and d'daughter and d'son, so before
I cracks up, I'm off to the mall liquor store."

"If twern't fer the youngsters," cried old Peter Dowd,
"I'd cancel the season, get rid of the crowd";
And yet, at the same time, we *all* know that he
Would be the first up to look under the tree.

Gord made me envy him, on that fine day,
When he bought his new girlfriend a sheer negligee;
I watched as he used all his wit and his charm
And talked the salesgirl into trying it on!

Poor Molly McGuire ran around in a spin,
Frantically searching for something for Jim;

"But the prices are vicious," she said in a snit,
"So I'll 'ave to go 'ome and knit a pair mitts."

Wally, the teacher, bought a hardcover book,
So his girlfriend could be a much better cook,
While Henry, the carpenter, took a big dare
And bought his good wife an aluminum square.

Big Myrtle Matthews was starting to fret
As she hurried to purchase her boyfriend a pet;
She got so confused by the slick-talking dealer
That she ended up buying a man-eating tiger.

Boys wanted hockey sticks, girls wanted dolls,
Women bought dresses, men, coveralls;
Those who were fat bought chocolate and stuff,
And those on a diet bought boxes of fluffs.

Visa and Master Cards all took a beatin'
As clerks pushed them through the magnetic readers;
Some people used cash, and some tried to deal,
While others used cheques, and some tried to steal.

"The poor fools," I thought, as I pitied them all
For falling into the trap of the mall;
Why can't they be sensible, use circumspection,
And not be consumed with such fickle temptation.

I went home to my house at the end of the day,
Thankful I wasn't caught up in the sway
Like so many suckers—when the thought came to me,
"I've no gift for the wife! I'm as dead as can be!"

'Twas the Day After Christmas
David Elliott

'Twas the day after Christmas in our fair town,
And me and the boys started making our rounds;
'Tis tradition, you know, to go visiting folks,
Drinkin' grog, eatin' turkey, and tellin' some jokes.

When Boxing Day comes there's a lot you can do,
Like visit with family or go on Ski-doo,
Toboggan or snowshoe, whatever you choose;
As for me and the boys, we go on the booze.

We got on the trot quite early that day—
Johnnie and Arthur and Billy and Ray,
Old Willy Waddle and Uncle Sam Bull,
Me and young Samson and Walt, the town fool.

Come twelve o'clock noon, poor Arthur was drunk,
So we carried him home, put him into his bunk;
His wife got dog-savage, was very dismayed,
'Cause Art was supposed to emcee the church play.

Ray looked at me as we left a friend's house,
Said, "Help me, ol' man—I'm as drunk as a louse";
And old Willy staggered, as we walked up the street,
Looking like someone who had two left feet.

Young Samson was doing real good for his age,
But come five o'clock he was starting to lag;
He wobbled and quivered and started to slouch,
So we left him alone coiled up on a couch.

Now Billy was yodelling (he'd had quite a drop),
While Uncle Sam Bull danced along with a mop;
But they got too rambunctious and started to shout,
So the man of the house we were in threw them out.

Johnnie, the show-off, was pleased with himself,
Said he could drink more than anyone else,
So he downed a full bottle of pure lemon gin
And ten minutes later wore only a grin.

With just me and Walt to keep up the fight,
We kept going on 'til late in the night;
I was glad I was able to keep up with his pace,
As I drank more and more and kept stuffing my face.

We ate codfish and toutins and turkey galore,
Salt chunk and cold praties, and then asked for more;
We drank whiskey and rum, hot toddies and wine,
And ended the day with a good belt of shine.

'Bout two in the morning we left one another;
I went to my house and Walt to his mother;
As we shook hands and parted, we said, with a slur,
"Lesh make sure we doos dis again come next yer."

My wife wasn't happy, and surely not pleased,
As I crawled up our path on my hands and my knees;
I tripped over the threshold, fell flat on my face,
And all that she told me was, "You're a disgrace!"

I went to the bedroom, hauled off my pants,
Fell on the mattress as if in a trance;
As I lay on the bed the light started to spin,
And I knew in the morning I'd pay for my sin.

The Hangover
David Elliott

The sun comes up, the alarm goes off,
The cat jumps out of the bed;
I open one eye and squint at the world—
Oh, what an ache in my head!

One foot falls out, the other hangs on,
Reluctant to leave its nest;
The body rebels and screams at the thought
Of leaving its haven of rest.

At last I'm up, but my joints are so stiff,
They grind and they crack and they creak;
My arms fail to move, my knees will not bend,
My voice refuses to speak.

Trembling, I reach the bathroom, and there
I stare in the mirror with fright;
I pull back in horror, I shake and I cringe
At the fearsome and hideous sight.

I feel and I poke, I touch and I check,
Making sure all my parts are in place;
I wash, and I comb, and after I shave,
I stick Cottonelle on my face.

With much trepidation, I move to the stairs
(After stubbing my toe on the bed);
My stomach is rumbling, my headache is throbbing—
I'm sure I'd be better off dead.

My forehead and hands are soaked with sweat;
I feel everything's closing in;
I look to my wife for some pity, instead
On her face is a dirty big grin.

To the table I stagger, I slump in a chair,
Not fit to be shot, it is clear;
My wife puts in front of me bacon and eggs,
Soaked in grease, then she says, "Enjoy, dear."

The yolks look so shiny (they mock as they slide
Back and forth on the rose-patterned plate),
When my stomach decides that it's time to get rid
Of the stuff that I drank and I ate.

There's not too much worse than fun in reverse,
Not much can compare with the pain;
So once more I swear to myself and the world;
No never, no never again!

Outport Memory
Minnie Jane Vallis

The howling sound
is forcing me
to twist and turn,
in search of peace.

I earnestly pray
for the sound to cease
and for silence once again
to fill the air.

Somewhere, buried deep
in my subconscious mind,
lie, dormant, fears
of another time,
when such a sound
struck terror in the heart
for loved ones out to sea.

There's none left now
that go to sea,
yet still the fear
of the howling winds
remains with me.

The Room
Marilyn Young

Nervously, I stood alone on the doorstep, hesitant to ring the doorbell. Would I be able to do what they asked of me? Would the little boy like me? As a live-in babysitter, I was spending the summer after high school away from family, friends and my hometown caring for a four-year-old boy.

Sucking in a deep breath, and raising my chin, I rang the bell. Just as the door opened, my purse slipped from my shoulder, falling to the white steps and spilling its contents everywhere.

I bent to retrieve my scattered items and found myself staring at a pair of dirty sneakers, topped by rolled-down white sports socks, which disappeared under a pair of faded jeans scuffed at the knees. Above this, a small, wiry frame was encased in a short white T-shirt. An angelic face with twinkling, mischievous eyes peered at me.

"Hi," I mumbled. "Is your mommy home?"

"Mom, it's her!" he hollered down a hallway which turned and disappeared into dimness.

A woman came out, smiling. "You must be our sitter for Jeremy," she said, holding out her hand. "Welcome to our home. Come in, come in."

The next hour was spent getting acquainted. Then it was Jeremy's bedtime. Following that, the next thing I knew, I was being gently awakened, unaware that I had fallen asleep as the woman had been talking to me.

"Come, I'll take you to your room," the woman said. "It appears you are very tired after your long trip on the bus." With that, she proceeded to lead me down a hallway with several doors leading into other rooms. I saw a child's room and a family room that seemed to have been arranged to match anyone's taste—games, television, music or reading.

"Here is your room," the woman announced as she pushed open a door. I stared wide-eyed at the surroundings. The words "your room, your room" kept echoing through my mind. Those words come back to haunt me over the years. Having grown up in a family of five brothers and five sisters, space and privacy were limited, precious items. "Go ahead; it's okay," she said. "I'll see you in the morning."

I changed my clothes and crawled into the bed. "Tomorrow, I'll look around," was my last thought.

I was awakened the next morning by chirping birds right outside my window. I slowly sat up and peered through the window. It looked out onto a small back garden typical of houses built in large cities. Few trees were evident, but from the few that grew in the garden, birds were calling for rain. The garden was green in patches, and a few flowers bloomed in a space along a picket fence.

Sitting back in bed, I surveyed my surroundings. I was lying on a double brass bed that was covered with a homemade quilt. Its main theme was yellow daffodils. The pattern was repeated in the curtains surrounding a large window and in the table skirt on the side table next to the bed. The table sported a goose-necked lamp, a radio clock and several books.

I crossed to a second door and tugged it open. On both sides, neatly arranged clothes hangers waited. I looked at my one small suitcase and thought: "What a waste of space!" Tucked in a corner was a roll-top desk; writing paper and a pen seemed to beckon me to sit and write a letter home.

I didn't join the family in the television room for most of that summer. Instead, I was contented to watch white fluffy clouds scatter across the sky while lying spread-eagled across the bed, trying to cover as much space as possible.

I remember the experience of closing a door and standing in a room alone. The fact that it only held one bed was a treat.

I felt awed that I could go to the closet, pull out a favourite sweater and realize I did not have to hunt for it or argue with someone about wearing my things.

I could change the furniture—no one complained! I could leave my bed unmade—no one minded! I could leave things around—they would not disappear mysteriously!

Since that summer, I have shared a room with a roommate and a three-bedroom apartment with five other girls while in college. After that came over twenty years of married life with a husband and two children.

Through all this, I felt something missing. Recently, I moved my son downstairs to a room I had converted into a bedroom and completely renovated his former room for my daughter.

In the process, I ended up with a spare room. Not really thinking about what I was doing, I moved my computer, desk and filing cabinet into this room. It was not until I heard my husband say, "I bought you a chair for your room" that it struck home.

My room! To do with as I please: change, close the door, compose, whatever strikes my fancy. My space— my own room!

Grandma, Please Tell Me
Minnie Jane Vallis

John Cabot was a master then;
The Matthew, steered by man,
'Gainst many a foe did defend
A wealthy new founde land.

Five hundred years and now we see
The fish are almost gone,
But Canada now holds the key
And waves the magic wand.

Folks say the stocks are ebbing fast;
I do profoundly wish
My grandchildren will never ask,

"Grandma, what's a fish?"

Biographies

Florence Antle, born in Pasadena and living in Deer Lake, says her inspiration to write comes from family and friends. About twelve years ago, she began her writing with a Christmas poem for her family.

Arthur M. Ball was born on April 10, 1912 in Northern Arm, Newfoundland. His parents were Sidney and Sarah and his wife was Mae, all deceased. His children are Myrna, Daphne, Robert and Earl. Arthur is retired from his work as a sign painter for Bowaters Ltd. Other works include poems and songs and many have been published.

Vincent Colin Burke, a native of St. Jacques and a graduate of St. Bonaventure's College in St. John's, retired April 30, 1988 from a twenty-two year career reporting (mostly on the courts and city council) for *The Western Star* in Corner Brook to write fiction and essays in Port au Port East. His first book, *Parracide and Other Weird Ploys: The Tales of Prester Nicol,* was published in May, 1997 by Commonwealth Productions Inc.

Sara Lynn Dussey is a thirteen year old Grade 8 student at St. Francis Xavier Junior High in Deer Lake, Newfoundland. "Apart from writing, I enjoy skating, travelling and trying new things. I enjoy writing because it allows me to express my point of view on different issues."

Amanda Caravan is a fourteen year old Grade 8 student at St. Francis Xavier Junior High in Deer Lake. "I enjoy writing poetry because it expresses the way I feel on certain topics." In her spare time, Amanda enjoys being with her friends and having a good time.

Pamela Chynn, 28, is a recent journalism graduate from Humber College in Etobicoke, Ontario. Prior to this, she received a Bachelor of Arts (English/Art History) from Carleton University. She has been published in several poetry magazines and anthologies and has co-written the book *You Don't Have to be a Brain Surgeon to Understand Liposuction*, with Tamara Fairchild. She is currently writing and living in downtown Toronto.

Madelyn Corbett started writing about thirty years ago when the Parish Players were formed; they wrote some of their own material. Since that time, she has written a little for the community through Guiding, the Strawberry Festival and the Parish Community. "Most of the writing that I have done through the years was for my family on special occasions."

David Elliott hated English and just about everyone and everything connected to it in his high school and university years. Around ten years ago, he was sitting at his desk when, to his utter astonishment, he realized that he enjoyed putting words on paper. Adopting the craft as a hobby, he has since written for a number of local magazines, and he is the author of the biography *Sailor White*. Now he is nervously compiling a collection of humour pieces, some of which appear in this anthology.

Vaughn Harbin, originally from St. John's, has lived in many places, including Rhode Island, Florida, Oklahoma,

Missouri and Quebec. Most of his writing reflects his "love for our great island home, Newfoundland, with its rocks, rivers, moors and mountains." The various communities in which he has lived and taught school in this province have provided him "with a wealth of experiences and images about which to write."

Jean Legge Hiscock writes "just for the fun of it." Her work has appeared in several publications. Her poem *Me Hog, Me Wife, A Wolf and Me* won her a second-place award in the Newfoundland and Labrador Arts and Letters Competition. She is a founding member of Page One.

Stacey M. Hiscock is a fourteen year old Grade 8 student at St. Francis Xavier Junior High in Deer Lake who lives in Reidville. She has been writing for as long as she can remember. Her poems have appeared in several publications and have won her an award.

Trina J. Hiscock lives in Deer Lake with her two young children who keep her quite busy, "but not too busy to write when the mood hits."

Brian J. Hoskins is a resident of Corner Brook who enjoys dabbling in writing. He is courageous enough to tackle both short fiction and poetry. His poems are usually centered around relationships.

Edith C. Johnson, a native Newfoundlander, enjoys the rugged natural beauty of her homeland. She is an enthusiastic reader of Newfoundland history and culture and has studied writing as a pupil of the Famous Writers School. She has been published in *Spawner*.

Danyelle Lavers has lived in Deer Lake all her life. She enjoys writing poetry. Her poems often deal with negative topics such as depression, sadness and pain. "Many young people have negative feelings and experiences and I hope my writing will help them deal with these experiences and issues."

Terry G. Manuel, a western Newfoundland writer, is currently working on a nonfiction account of his real-life experiences. He writes to express the way he feels about the way things are.

Amber Milley is a student at Pasadena Academy. She writes because "it feels good to finish a story and it helps to get my thoughts out." She also sings in her brother Steven's rock band.

Terri Moores was born in St. John's and has lived in Deer Lake with her large supportive family for the past fourteen years. She delights in playing sports, participating in group activities, travelling and writing. She writes to express feelings, moods, and actions and is inspired from within and by others. As one of the highest ranked Deer Lake Sea Cadets, she has learned that she can "be all that I can be, show leadership, moral, esprit de corps, responsibility and discipline." She believes "anyone can succeed, but only if they believe."

Billy Parsons was born in Newfoundland, but spent his first four years in Nova Scotia. Since 1988, he and his family have lived in Deer Lake. He is a Grade 7 student at the Deer Lake Pentecostal School. He enjoys drawing and hopes to become a professional comic artist. Billy's poems reflect his "many interests and love of the unusual."

Sarah Penney-Flynn is a 1997 graduate of Pasadena Academy. She has written several pieces for local publication. She writes to unleash personal thoughts and voices. "The blood of my writing," she says, "comes from my own personal struggles." One of her poems, *Beneath the Harvest Moon*, was published by the National Library of Poetry.

Iovana Pye was born on October 29, 1975 in Corner Brook, daughter of Yolanda Russell. She was educated at Elwood Regional High in Deer Lake and works as a hostess at Tim Hortons in Deer Lake. Iovana says "I love to read Stephen King novels and I write poetry as a hobby as does my grandmother and great grandfather."

Daphne Russell was born on February 22, 1937 in Deer Lake to Arthur and Mae Ball. She and her husband Paul had five children: Paul Jr., Yolanda, Tad, Ina, Lorinda and Svein. She was educated at Deer Lake Academy and worked for twenty-two years as a mail courier. She is now a homemaker. She is of the Pentecostal faith. Her hobbies include volunteer work, sports, craft-making and politics. She writes poetry and short stories and has had several published. "Writing is a gift from God. I just want to say thank you, God for all the beautiful gifts in life."

Ronald T. Smith was born in St. John's on July 4th,

1937 and moved to Deer Lake in 1965. Except for brief stints in Montreal and on Vancouver Island, Deer Lake has become his adopted home. He received his early journalistic training from The Newspaper Institute of America in Chicago and later studied Photo Journalism at Malaspina College on Vancouver Island. His work has appeared in company trade magazines, *Reader's Digest*, and in the '70's and '80's, he served as local correspondent for *The Western Star*. During the late '80's and early '90's, he published the Deer Lake weekly *The Lakeside Press*. He is owner/operator of Deer Lake Printing & Stationery.

W. Rex Stirling writes poetry, songs, short stories, reviews, interviews, and promotional copy for radio. His work has appeared in the *British Motorcycling Federation Monthly, Canadian Biker, USA Rider, Newfoundland Herald, DOWNHOMER, The Western Star*, and other publications.

Natasha Strickland, born in Grand Falls, Newfoundland is a 15 year-old honours student at Deer Lake Pentecostal School. She enjoys reading, hanging out with friends, horse-back riding, playing basketball, Sea Cadets, and most of all, writing. She lives with her aunt, uncle, and older brother. Her favourite food is pizza, her favourite colour is blue, she loves animals and enjoys writing poems and stories "about everything in life."

Janalee A. Strowbridge is a graphic artist. She was a winner in the Newfoundland and Labrador Arts and Letters competition for her poem *Two of a Kind*.

Nellie P. Strowbridge, a former newspaper and magazine columnist, has won numerous writing awards, including Canada's Stamp of Approval Award. Her book *Widdershins: Stories of a Fisherman's Daughter* has made its way across the continent. She is included in several anthologies and is one of three women writers featured in *Doors Held Ajar*. "I write what I feel, hoping my readers will feel what I write."

Minnie Jane Vallis, nee Kendall, was born in the town of Ramea, a fishing community. She has written for school, church, and community projects but this is her first publication. She is "a proud Newfoundlander first, and a Canadian second." For her, "writing is a creative process that keeps the soul from withering."

D. Jean Young explores different ideas and lives through her writing. Her fiction and non-fiction work has appeared in several publications. Jean is a founding member of Page One. She actively encourages other writers. Her book *Quicksilver Summer*, a series of writings for young people, will be published in the fall of 1998.

Marilyn Young is a former reporter and columnist for *The Western Star*. Her writing also includes work as an information officer for the Western Newfoundland Model Forest. She is a founding member of Page One and is currently looking for avenues to do freelance writing.

ORDERING INFORMATION

To order another copy (s) of Page One Digest, send a cheque or money order with your name and address, to:

> PAGE ONE DIGEST
> P.O. Box 3036
> Deer Lake, NF Canada
> A0K 2E0

Enclose $ 10.00 for each copy of the book plus $ 3.00 for shipping and handling for each order.

Please allow four weeks for delivery.

1511